MATHEMA

A MASTER FILE
KEY STAGE 2

Editors

D C Perkins, BA (Hons), MEd, PhD (Wales) and E J Perkins, BSc (Hons), MEd

Illustrations by Anthony James

These Master Files are designed for use in the classroom. Each consists of teachers' notes, pupils' resource material, worksheets, activities and record sheet. Each book covers a part of the national curriculum in depth allowing the teacher to decide the amount of material to use according to the age and ability of the children.

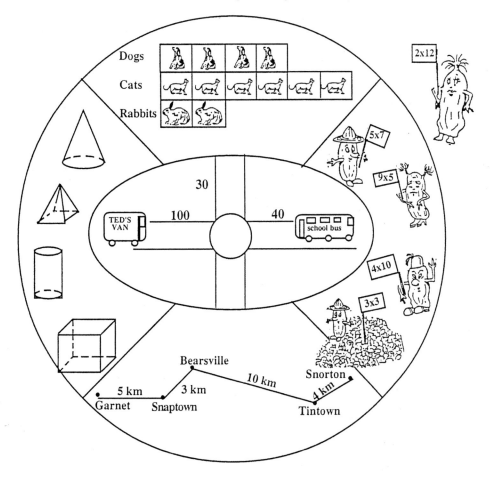

DOMINO BOOKS (WALES) LTD
SWANSEA SA1 1 FN
Tel. 01792 459378   Fax. 01792 466337

Mathematics Master File KS2 © EJP & DCP 1993 Reprinted 1994, 1995, 1996, 1997, 1998, 1999. Revised 2000
ISBN 1 85772 086 5

CONTENTS 1

PUPILS' RESOURCES/WORKSHEETS

Teachers' Notes and Resources Contents on next page.

CONTENTS 2

TEACHER'S NOTES AND RESOURCES

HOW TO USE YOUR MASTER FILE

For many experienced teachers these few lines will seem superfluous. This book follows the guidelines of the National Curriculum. The scope of the material taught in mathematics today has widened considerably and the emphasis on relating the subject to 'real' situations in the 'real' world makes the subject less mysterious and of more obvious use. A sound understanding of the fundamental theory is essential but so is an awareness that tedious repetition creates nothing but boredom. It is when children are little, when everything is new that the foundations of mathematical ability are developed, interest generated or lost. Some of the worksheets are more difficult than others and there is plenty of material that all will find fun to tackle and other work that is more challenging. We do not envisage any problems selecting appropriate material.

1. All the material in this book is photocopiable as defined on the first page. This means that all the material can be used in any way you wish in the classroom situation. Drawings any be photocopied and adapted for further work.

2. Covering sections of the master copies with plain paper enables resource material to be used in different ways.

3. Reduction of the A4 master copies to A5 means that they can be pasted in children's exercise books. The master copies can also be enlarged to A3 making it easier for students to work on them as a group.

4. Some of the photocopies can be cut to make additional puzzles and games.

5. It is intended that the material should be used selectively depending on the ages and abilities of your pupils.

6. Much of the completed work may be used as visual aids around the classroom.

7. Remember, there are often several ways in which problems can be tackled.

8. Project work may be done individually, in groups and/or with teacher participation.

9. Mathematics is important in most subjects and these links underpin some of the reasons for learning the subject. There is latitude and longitude and navigation in geography, dating discoveries in history and archaeology and making computer pictures of what they were like . . . Concepts learned now are essential later in engineering, architecture, economics, all the sciences . . . Where practical, links with other subjects should be used.

10. Mathematics is about pattern, sorting, classifying and organising. Much of the work in this book can be used to illustrate the importance of these skills in the 'real' world.

We hope you enjoy using this book and welcome any comments.

ADDITION TO 10

Write down how many apples in numbers and words. The first one has been done for you.

Apples	Number	Word
(three apples)	3	Three
(five apples)		
(nine apples)		

How many? Put the answers in the boxes.

 and make ☐

 and (mushrooms) make ☐

(two figures) and (four figures) make

Put dots on these dominoes. How many dots on each one? The first one has been done or you.

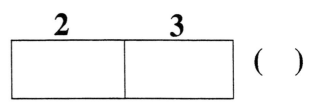

3 | **4**   (7)

2 | **3**   ( )

6 | **2**   ( )

1 | **5**   ( )

2 | **7**   ( )

Look at this number line. What number goes in each box? The first has been done for you.

| 1 | 2 | ☐ | 4 | ☐ | ☐ | 7 | ☐ | ☐ | 10 |

Write down the pairs of numbers which make 10. The first one has been done for you.

| 1 | 2 | 3 | 4 | 5 | 6 | 7 | 8 | 9 | 10 |

1 and **9** make **10**   and   make **10**

2 and   make **10**   **5** and   make **10**

3 and   make **10**

Write the answers as words and then as numbers

one + three   ___four___ **4**

two + one   _____

four + two   _____

three + five   _____

six + one   _____

eight + one   _____

one + seven   _____

two + eight   _____

three + three   _____

five + three   _____

Write down the answers to these sums

2 + 4 = _____

3 + 7 = _____

4 + 5 = _____

1 + 7 = _____

6 + 2 = _____

3 + 3 = _____

4 + 6 = _____

2 + 1 + 2 = _____

2 + 2 + 1 = _____

3 + 5 + 1 = _____

5 + 3 + 1 = _____

Count the people in the carriages of this train.

How many people in carriage A? ☐

How many people in carriage B? ☐

How many people in all the carriages? ☐

SUBTRACTION TO 10

1. **Here are five apples.**

    Take three apples away.

    How many are left?
    Write the answer in the box

2. **Take away two apples.**

3. **You may find it easier to work out these problems if you draw the apples. Write your answers in the boxes.**

Three apples take away one apple leaves

Four apples take away two apples leaves

5 apples take away 2 apples leaves

7 apples take away 3 apples leaves

8 apples take away 3 apples leaves

4 apples minus 1 apple leaves

6 apples minus 2 apples leaves

SUBTRACTION TO 10/FEWER

1. **5 take away 2 leaves** _____

2. **Now try these**

   5 - 2 = _____   6 - 4 = _____

   4 - 2 = _____   3 - 1 = _____

   7 - 4 = _____   2 - 1 = _____

   9 - 1 = _____   10 - 6 = _____

   8 - 6 = _____   10 - 8 = _____

3. **Look at the train at the bottom of the page. Write the answers to the questions in the boxes.**

   Which carriage has the most people in it?

   Which carriage has the fewest people in it?

   How many more people are there in carriage A than in carriage B?

   How many more people are there in carriage A than in carriage C?

   How many fewer people are there in carriage C than in A?

   How many fewer people are there in carriage B than in A?

   When the train stops, 2 people leave carriage B and 1 gets into carriage B.
   Which carriages now have the same number of people in them?

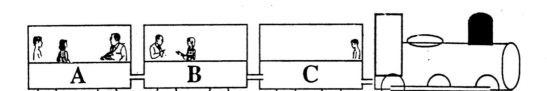

ADDITION AND SUBTRACTION

1.

Dogs	🐕	🐕	🐕	🐕		
Cats	🐈	🐈	🐈	🐈	🐈	🐈
Rabbits	🐇	🐇				

This chart shows how many animals are in an animal hospital.

How many dogs are in the hospital? ☐

How many cats? ☐

How many more cats than dogs? ☐

How many rabbits? ☐

How many animals altogether? ☐

Make a chart for Jane who has two cats, three dogs and a pony.

2. A box contains 2 pencils. 3 are added. How many are in the box now? ☐

3. A man buys tickets for a football match for himself, his three children and a friend. How many tickets does he buy? ☐

4. There are 5 cakes on a plate, 3 are eaten. How many are left? ☐

5. A dog has 6 puppies. 4 are given away. How many are kept? ☐

6. Colin has 10 sweets. He eats 2 and gives 1 to his friend. How many are left? ☐

7. A hen lays 7 eggs. 1 is boiled, 2 are fried and 1 is broken. How many are left? ☐

8. There are 2 boys and 3 girls on a bus. When the bus stops a boy and a girl get off. How many children are left on the bus? ☐

TENS AND UNITS

1. **Fill in the tens and units then write the numbers under the boxes. The first one has been done for you.**

tens	units
† † † †	• • •
4	**3**

__43__

tens	units
† † † † †	• • • • • •

_____

tens	units
† † † † † † †	• • • • •

_____

tens	units
† † † † † † †	•

_____

2. **How many units are there in these numbers? The first one has been done for you.**

53 has | **3** units | **42** has | units | **28** has | units |

3. **How many tens are there in these numbers?**

61 has | tens | **29** has | tens | **75** has | tens |

4. **These are a bit harder.**

27 has | tens and units | **96** has | tens and units |

DICE/MONEY

1. Add the totals on these dice.

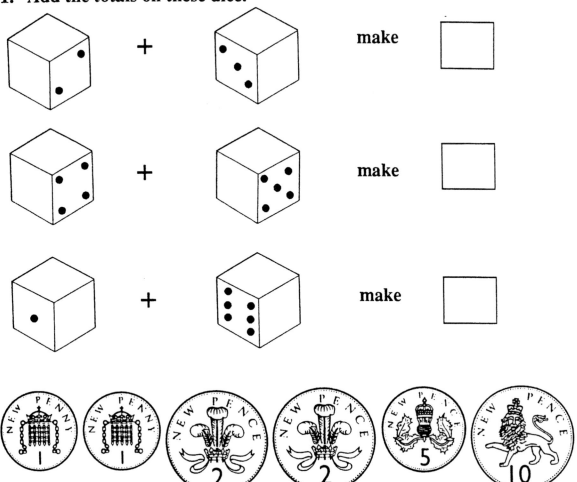

   +   make

   +   make

   +   make

Choose any three of the coins above to make each of the amounts below.
Write the coins you pick in the circles.

8p = ◯ ◯ ◯   14p = ◯ ◯ ◯

9p = ◯ ◯ ◯   16p = ◯ ◯ ◯

13p = ◯ ◯ ◯   17p = ◯ ◯ ◯

ORDERING AND PLACE VALUE

1. Put these numbers in order beginning with the smallest.

42, 7, 65, 31, 3, 29, 11, 24, 92, 50

_____

2. Now try these. The first one has been done for you.

Two more than 8 is _____10_____

One less than 7 is _____

One less than 4 is _____

One less than 9 is _____

Five more than 4 is _____

Eight more than 1 is _____

The difference between 9 and 3 is _____

The difference between 6 and 1 is _____

3. Look at the numbers

24, 40, 69, 8, 33, 20, 11, 27, 92, 5

The smallest is _____

The biggest is _____

The number with a 4 in the tens column is _____

The number with a 5 in the units column is _____

The number smaller than 27 and bigger than 20 is _____

The number with the same figure in the tens and units columns is _____

SHOPPING AND CHANGE

These items are for sale in the school shop

A bar of chocolate costs   _____

2 cans of FIZO cost   _____

A can of FIZO and a cake cost   _____

3 cans of FIZO cost   _____

3 bars of chocolate cost   _____

2 cans of FIZO, 2 cakes and a bar of chocolate cost   _____

2 cakes cost   _____
I pay with two coins. What are they?   _____ and _____

A bar of chocolate and a can of FIZO cost   _____
I pay with three coins. What are they?   _____

How much change is left from 5p if I buy a cake?   _____
I am given two coins as change. What are they?   _____

How much change is left from 20 p if I buy 2 cans of FIZO and a cake?   _____
For my change I am given three coins. What are they?

_____

I have 9p. What can I buy that will use up ALL my money?

_____   or   _____

HALF AND QUARTER

1. **Colour half of each drawing red and the other half blue.**

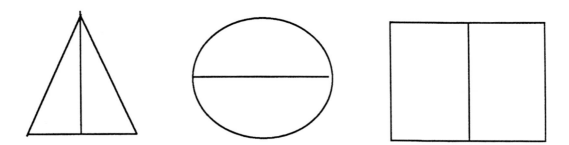

2. **Colour a quarter of each drawing green.**

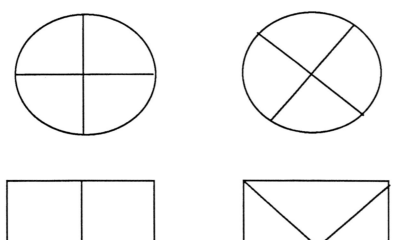

3. **What fraction is shaded in each drawing?**

FRACTIONS

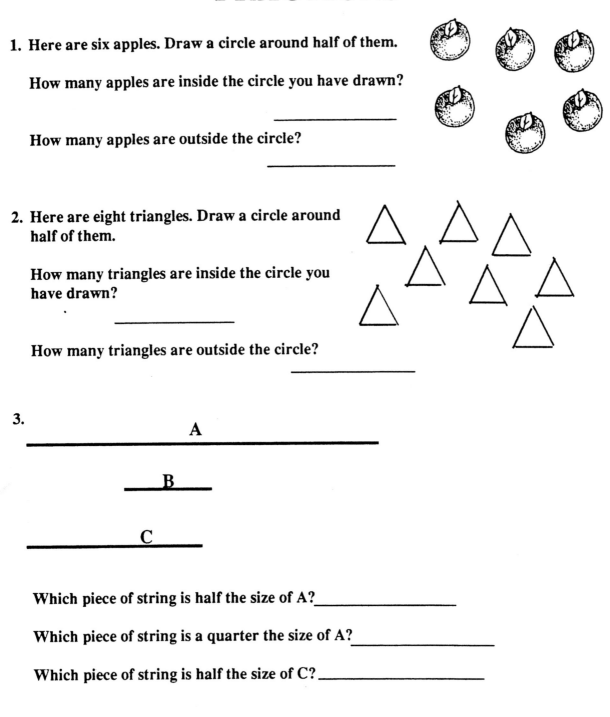

1. Here are six apples. Draw a circle around half of them.

   How many apples are inside the circle you have drawn?

   _____

   How many apples are outside the circle?

   _____

2. Here are eight triangles. Draw a circle around half of them.

   How many triangles are inside the circle you have drawn?

   _____

   How many triangles are outside the circle?

   _____

3.

   _____ A _____

   _____ B _____

   _____ C _____

   Which piece of string is half the size of A?_____

   Which piece of string is a quarter the size of A?_____

   Which piece of string is half the size of C? _____

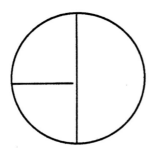

4. Colour half of this circle red, one quarter green and one quarter yellow.

MEASURING

1. Use your hand to measure the top of your desk.

2. Walk around your classroom and use your feet to measure the length and breadth of the room.

3. Walk around the playground and count the number of strides you take.

   Do you expect everyone in the class to have the same results? Give a reason for your answer.

DESK

CLASSROOM

PLAYGROUND

4.

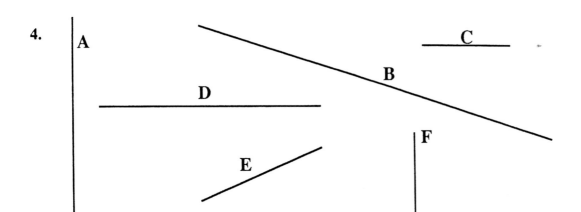

Study these lines

Which is the longer vertical line? _____

Which is the shorter horizontal line? _____

Which is the longer sloping line? _____

Use your ruler to find the lengths of the lines in cm.

What is the difference in length between (i) lines B and A (ii) lines E and F?

(i) _____ (ii) _____

Which lines are the same length? _____

5.

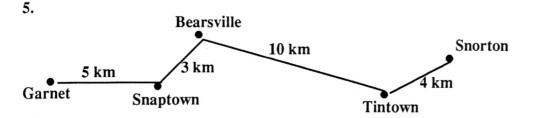

This map shows the distances between five towns.

How far is Snaptown from Garnet? _____

How far is it to Bearsville from Garnet through Snaptown? _____

How far is Bearsville from Tintown? _____

How far is Snorton from Tintown? _____

Which two towns are closest to each other? _____

How much nearer is Snorton to Tintown than Bearsville is to Tintown? _____

PLACE VALUE AND ORDERING TO 1000

Circle the correct answers

Twenty four is	42	420	24	204	240
Thirty nine is	30	139	93	39	309
One hundred and thirty one is	133	131	130	103	113
Three hundred is	3	30	300	303	3000
One hundred and two is	112	120	122	102	1200
One more than 20 is	201	12	21	211	200
One less than 40 is	30	3	39	140	401
Three more than 40 is	403	430	4003	43	4030
One less than 100 is	11	99	109	91	101
Two less than 272 is	27	72	270	252	274
The number bigger than 35 but smaller than 37 is	351	367	36	34	38
The number between 99 and 101 is	919	909	100	109	190

Look at these numbers. Put them in order beginning with the smallest and ending with the biggest. Then answer the questions below.

24, 3, 561, 98, 601, 198, 400, 970, 11, 79

_____

Which number has 4 in the units place? _____

Which numbers have 9 in the tens place? _____ and _____

Which number has 6 in the hundreds place? _____

Which number is smaller than 10? _____

Which number is bigger than 900 but smaller than 1 000? _____

ADDITION AND SUBTRACTION TO 20

Work out these sums.

$8 + 11 =$ _____

$5 + 6 + 2 =$ _____

$4 + 9 + 3 =$ _____

$1 + 0 + 17 =$_____

$7 + 9 + 2 =$_____

$18 - 5 =$ _____

$20 - 3 =$ _____

$10 - 4 =$ _____

$17 - 6 =$ _____

$13 - 4 =$ _____

$4 + 6 - 3 =$ _____

$5 - 2 + 0 =$ _____

$3 - 1 + 9 =$ _____

$2 + 4 - 1 =$ _____

$3 + 12 - 4 =$ _____

$2 + 18 - 5 =$ _____

$7 - 4 + 15 =$ _____

$5 - 8 + 4 =$ _____

$4 - 6 + 14 =$ _____

$0 - 5 + 9 =$ _____

Find the missing numbers

$3 +$ ⬚ $= 8$

$12 +$ ⬚ $= 19$

$11 +$ ⬚ $= 17$

$13 -$ ⬚ $= 5$

$10 -$ ⬚ $= 7$

$19 -$ ⬚ $= 16$

$4 + 3 +$ ⬚ $= 14$

$7 + 4 -$ ⬚ $= 6$

$9 -$ ⬚ $+ 5 = 10$

$3 +$ ⬚ $+ 4 = 7$

$12 -$ ⬚ $- 4 = 6$

Complete the following

$$\begin{array}{r} 1\ \ 2 \\ 5\ + \\ \hline \end{array} \qquad \begin{array}{r} 1\ \ 3 \\ 6\ + \\ \hline \end{array}$$

_____   _____

$$\begin{array}{r} 1\ \ 0 \\ 9\ + \\ \hline \end{array} \qquad \begin{array}{r} 1\ \ 1 \\ 3\ + \\ \hline \end{array}$$

_____   _____

$$\begin{array}{r} 1\ \ 7 \\ 1\ \ 0\ - \\ \hline \end{array} \qquad \begin{array}{r} 1\ \ 4 \\ 2\ - \\ \hline \end{array}$$

_____   _____

PROBLEMS

1   John has 12 sweets. He eats 2 and gives 3 to a friend. How
    many are left?

    1 [   ]

2   Mary has a red crayon, 2 blue crayons and 3 green ones.
    How many crayons does she have altogether?

    2 [   ]

3   Mark's dog has 3 puppies. He finds a home for 2 of them.
    How many are left?

    3 [   ]

4   There are 10 lights on a Christmas tree. 2 go out. How many
    are still lit?

    4 [   ]

5   Cardiff City score 2 goals and Cambridge City score 1 goal.
    How many goals were scored altogether?

    5 [   ]

6   One day, John works 3 hours and the next day he works
    7 hours. How long does he work in total?

    6 [   ]

7   Arthur is 12 and Jack is two years older. How old is Jack?

    7 [   ]

8   Jennifer has 19 marbles and June has 11. How many more
    marbles does Jennifer have than June?

    8 [   ]

9   Gillian invited five boys and four girls to her birthday party.
    One of the girls was ill. How many children, including Gillian,
    were at the party? How many more boys than girls were
    there?

    9 [   ]

10 Ann is 5 years older than her brother, James. When James is
    4, how old is Ann?

    10 [   ]

11 If Paul was three years older, he would be the same age as
    Martin who is 14. How old is Paul?

    11 [   ]

12 What is the difference between 11 and 7?

    12 [   ]

13 What number is 10 more than 27?

    13 [   ]

14 What number is 9 less than 23?

    14 [   ]

15 Phillip has 35 football stickers and his friend, Anthony
    has 47. (i) How many more stickers does Anthony have than
    Phillip?(ii) How many stickers must Anthony give Phillip
    if both boys are to have the same number?
    (iii) How many stickers do they need to have a total of 100?

    15
    i [   ]

    ii [   ]

    iii[   ]

16 John has test marks of 40, 24, 35 and 60.
    Jane has marks of 43, 22, 38 and 55.
    Who has the most marks in total and by how many?

    16 [   ]

PLACE VALUE CARDS

Paste these cards on to a piece of cardboard, cut them out and put them into a bag.
Make several base boards from a picture with numbers on it. (See next page.) Take the
number cards from the bag and try to match the cards with the numbers on the board.
The first to cover all the numbers on his or her board is the winner.

units	units	units	units	units	units	units	units	units	units
0	1	2	3	4	5	6	7	8	9
units	units	units	units	units	units	units	units	units	units
0	1	2	3	4	5	6	7	8	9
units	units	units	units	units	units	units	units	units	units
0	1	2	3	4	5	6	7	8	9
tens	tens	tens	tens	tens	tens	tens	tens	tens	tens
0	1	2	3	4	5	6	7	8	9
tens	tens	tens	tens	tens	tens	tens	tens	tens	tens
0	1	2	3	4	5	6	7	8	9
tens	tens	tens	tens	tens	tens	tens	tens	tens	tens
0	1	2	3	4	5	6	7	8	9
hundreds	hundreds	hundreds	hundreds	hundreds	hundreds	hundreds	hundreds	hundreds	hundreds
0	1	2	3	4	5	6	7	8	9
hundreds	hundreds	hundreds	hundreds	hundreds	hundreds	hundreds	hundreds	hundreds	hundreds
0	1	2	3	4	5	6	7	8	9
hundreds	hundreds	hundreds	hundreds	hundreds	hundreds	hundreds	hundreds	hundreds	hundreds
0	1	2	3	4	5	6	7	8	9

PLACE VALUE BOARDS

Find the place value cards for these numbers. For example for 206 you need

hundreds	tens	units
2	**0**	**6**

The game is quicker if only the place value cards needed are 'put in the bag'.

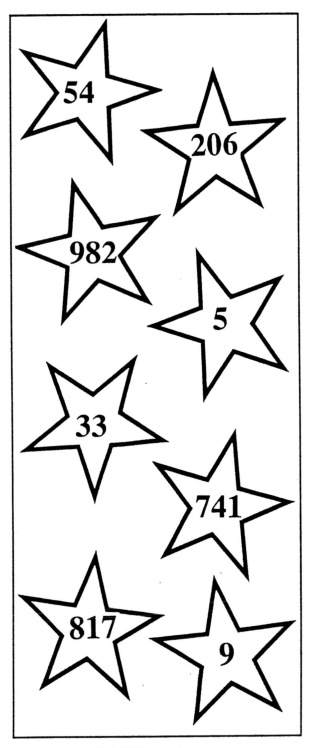

PAIR BONDS TO 20
NUMBER PATTERNS

These are two number lines to 20. Add them up and then answer the questions below.

0	1	2	3	4	5	6	7	8	9	10	11	12	13	14	15
20	19	18	17	16	15	14	13	12	11	10	9	8	7	6	5

20 20 20 20 20 20

16	17	18	19	20
4	3	2	1	0

How many pairs of numbers add up to 20?

0 and   make 20   6 and   make 20

1 and   make 20   7 and   make 20

2 and   make 20   8 and   make 20

3 and   make 20   9 and   make 20

4 and   make 20   10 and   make 20

5 and   make 20   Why does the table stop here?

1   ②   3   ④
5   6   7   8
9   10   11   12
13   14   15   16
17   18   19   20

Beginning with 2, circle every second number.
Now count to 20 in twos.

2,   4,   6,

BINGO

Paste the bingo and caller cards on to cardboard and cut out. Mix the caller cards and place in a pile face down. Choose a caller. The caller turns over the cards one at a time and calls out the numbers. The children cover the numbers on their bingo cards which make twenty with the numbers called. For example, if 3 is called, then 17 is covered on the bingo cards. The game is more fun if the children work in pairs. The winners are those who cover their bingo card first. The class can make their own bingo cards.

BINGO CARDS

2	17	19	13
11	5	6	18
1	3	7	12
15	4	16	9

18	14	6	2
9	16	10	4
11	3	12	1
13	8	15	7

CALLER CARDS

1	11
2	12
3	13
4	14
5	15
6	16
7	17
8	18
9	19
10	

FIVE AND TEN TIMES TABLES

Circle every fifth number to make the pattern of the five times table.

1	2	3	4	⑤	6	7	8	9	⑩
11	12	13	14	⑮	16	17	18	19	20
21	22	23	24	25	26	27	28	29	30
31	32	33	34	35	36	37	38	39	40
41	42	43	44	45	46	47	48	49	50
51	52	53	54	55	56	57	58	59	60

Use the number square to find out

4 times 5 = _____

5 times 5 = _____

7 x 5 = _____

9 x 5 = _____

Count to 60 in fives.   5, 10, _____

Circle every tenth number to make the pattern of the tens times table.

1	2	3	4	5	6	7	8	9	⑩
11	12	13	14	15	16	17	18	19	⑳
21	22	23	24	25	26	27	28	29	㉚
31	32	33	34	35	36	37	38	39	40
41	42	43	44	45	46	47	48	49	50
51	52	53	54	55	56	57	58	59	60
61	62	63	64	65	66	67	68	69	70
71	72	73	74	75	76	77	78	79	80
81	82	83	84	85	86	87	88	89	90
91	92	93	94	95	96	97	98	99	100
101	102	103	104	105	106	107	108	109	110
111	112	113	114	115	116	117	118	119	120

Use the number square to find out

3 times 10 = _____

5 times 10 = _____

8 x 10 = _____

10 x 10 = _____

12 x 10 = _____

Count to 120 in tens.   10, 20, _____

MULTIPLICATION - QUESTION CARDS

Paste these Question Cards on to board and cut them out. Shuffle them and match them to the Answer Cards.

2 x 1 =	2 x 2 =	2 x 3 =	2 x 4 =	2 x 5 =
2 x 6 =	2 x 7 =	2 x 8 =	2 x 9 =	2 x 10 =
2 x 11 =	2 x 12 =	5 x 1 =	5 x 2 =	5 x 3 =
5 x 4 =	5 x 5 =	5 x 6 =	5 x 7 =	5 x 8 =
5 x 9 =	5 x 10 =	5 x 11 =	5 x 12 =	10 x 1 =
10 x 2 =	10 x 3 =	10 x 4 =	10 x 5 =	10 x 6 =
10 x 7 =	10 x 8 =	10 x 9 =	10 x 10 =	10 x 11 =
10 x 12 =	3 x 3 =	4 x 3 =	4 x 4 =	3 x 2 =

MULTIPLICATION - ANSWER CARDS

Paste these Answer Cards on to board and cut them out. Match them to the Question Cards.

2	4	6	8	10
12	14	16	18	20
22	24	5	10	15
20	25	30	35	40
45	50	55	60	10
20	30	40	50	60
70	80	90	100	110
120	9	12	16	6

MULTIPLICATION

4 x 5 = 20   5 x 4 = 20   2 x 10 = 20   10 x 2 = 20

The answer to all these multiplications is 20. Find all the multiplications to give the answers below.

Answer	Multiplications
4	
12	
15	
16	
20	**4 x 5 5 x 4 2 x 10 10 x 2**
30	
35	
40	
60	

DIVISION - QUESTION CARDS

Paste these Question Cards on to board and cut them out. Shuffle them and match them to the Answer Cards.

$2 \div 2 =$	$4 \div 2 =$	$6 \div 2 =$	$8 \div 2 =$	$10 \div 2 =$
$12 \div 2 =$	$14 \div 2 =$	$16 \div 2 =$	$18 \div 2 =$	$20 \div 2 =$
$22 \div 2 =$	$24 \div 2 =$	$5 \div 5 =$	$10 \div 5 =$	$15 \div 5 =$
$20 \div 5 =$	$25 \div 5 =$	$30 \div 5 =$	$35 \div 5 =$	$40 \div 5 =$
$45 \div 5 =$	$50 \div 5 =$	$55 \div 5 =$	$60 \div 5 =$	$10 \div 10 =$
$20 \div 10 =$	$30 \div 10 =$	$40 \div 10 =$	$50 \div 10 =$	$60 \div 10 =$
$70 \div 10 =$	$80 \div 10 =$	$90 \div 10 =$	$100 \div 10 =$	$110 \div 10 =$
$120 \div 10 =$	$9 \div 3 =$	$12 \div 3 =$	$16 \div 4 =$	$20 \div 4 =$

DIVISION - ANSWER CARDS

Paste these Answer Cards on to board and cut them out. Shuffle them and match them to the Question Cards.

1	2	3	4	5
6	7	8	9	10
11	12	1	2	3
4	5	6	7	8
9	10	11	12	1
2	3	4	5	6
7	8	9	10	11
12	3	4	4	5

PROBLEMS

1. Find the cost of 4 theatre tickets at £4 each. _____

2. John has 12 sweets to share between himself and his two friends. How many sweets does each have? _____

3. Mark has £1 for pocket money. He spends 25p on ice cream and 30p on a magazine. How much does he have left? _____

4. Tommy is saving for a new bike. He saves £5 a month for a year. On his birthday he is given £30 in presents and at Christmas he is given £20. If the bike costs £125, how much more money does he have to save?

    _____

5. A Car Boot Sale raises £22 towards the cost of a seaside trip. The return journey on the bus to the seaside costs £3. How many bus tickets can be bought? _____
    If each child on the trip is given £5 spending money, how much does the trip cost?

    _____

6. A man needs 3 litres of paint to decorate a room. The paint is sold in half litre cans at £3 a can. How many cans of paint must he buy and what is the total cost? _____

7. A baker needs 7 kg of flour which is sold in 2 kg bags at 90p a bag. How many bags of flour must he buy and how much do they cost?

    _____

8. A car travels 25 miles on a gallon of petrol. How many gallons must the motorist buy for a journey of 110 miles? _____

9. John invites 7 friends to a party. His mother buys several boxes of cakes each containing 6 cakes. How many boxes must she buy if John and his friends are to have at least 2 cakes each?

    _____

10. The budget for printing football programmes for a match is £20. If the programmes cost 10p each, how many can be printed?

    _____

ESTIMATES/UNITS

1. Who is the tallest in your class? _____

2. Who is the shortest in your class? _____

3. Who has the longest hair? _____

4. Who has the shortest hair? _____

5. What is the length and breadth of the top of your desk? _____

6. What is the height of the classroom door? _____

7. What is the width of the widest window in the classroom? _____

8. Who lives nearest to the school? _____

9. Who lives furthest from the school? _____

10. How many books are in the classroom library? _____

11. How thick is the thickest book in the library? _____

    How thin is the thinnest? _____

12. What is the breadth of the classroom? _____

13. What is the length of the playground? _____

14. Your height is measured in cm. What are the units for the following?

    Milk is measured in _____   Petrol is measured in _____

    Money is measured in _____   A day is measured in _____

    The height of a pony is measured in _____

    The rate at which a person walks is measured in _____

    The speed at which a car travels is measured in _____

    The height at which an aeroplane flies is measured in _____

    The age of a baby (less than a year old) is measured in _____ or _____

    The age of an adult is measured in _____

15. Fill in the spaces.
    My mother bought 2 _____ of sugar, 500 _____ of low fat margarine

    and 2 _____ of orange juice.

    She also bought 10 _____ of petrol and 1 _____ of oil for the car.

CAR BOOT SALE

This is a selection of some of the things you might bring to sell or buy. Price cards are on the next page but don't forget to barter as well. 2 squares are left blank for you to draw your special bargains.

DOLL	CLOCK	SKITTLES	DINOSAUR	DINOSAUR EGGS
CAMERA	GERBIL	TEDDY	VAN	LANTERN
CAKES	BUS	APPLES	CRAYONS	DRAGON
HOUSE	HAT	DRUM	MUGS	BOAT
PLANTS	RUGBY BALL	CRICKET BAT	BOOKS	CONCORDE
TRAIN	BUCKET AND SPADE	SHOES		

PRICE TAGS

These are suggested price tags. Some are left blank for you to write your own prices.
Don't forget special offers and bargain prices.

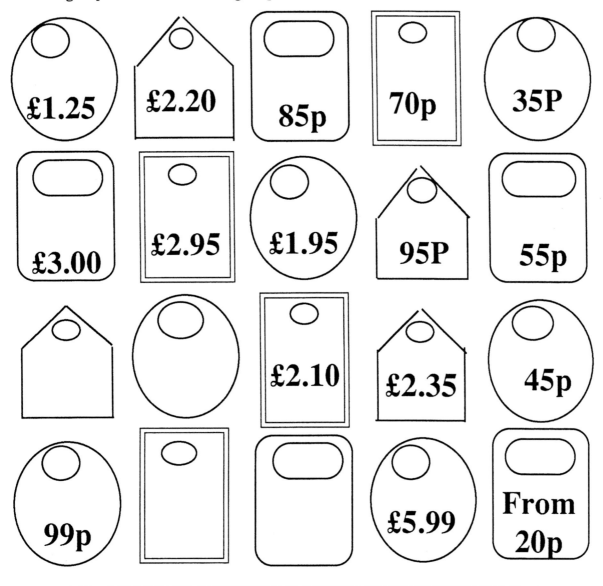

£1.25 £2.20 85p 70p 35P

£3.00 £2.95 £1.95 95P 55p

£2.10 £2.35 45p

99p £5.99 From 20p

ALL PRICES HALVED

BARGAINS

10% REDUCTION ON STAR GOODS

15P OFF ALL MARKED PRICES

TIME

1. What time did you get up? _____

2. What time does school start in the morning? _____

3. What time do you leave school at the end of the day? _____

4. What time do you arrive home after school? _____

5. How long does it take you to travel from school to your home? _____

6. There are three ways in which we tell the time. For example on a traditional or analogue clock we say quarter past one (in the day) or 1. 15 pm and on a 24-hour digital clock this is 13.15. (There are also 24 hour analogue clocks.) Fill in the spaces and draw the hands on the analogue clock face. The first set has been done for you.

ANALOGUE		DIGITAL
Quarter past one (afternoon)	1.15 pm	13.15
_____	10.00 am	_____
_____	_____	23.30

7. What times do you put into a video recorder (with a 24-hour digital clock) to make it record
   (i). a programme starting at 7 o'clock in the morning and lasting for 55 minutes?

Recording begins at _____ and ends at _____

   (ii). a film beginning at 11.30 in the evening and lasting for 90 minutes?

Recording begins at _____ and ends at _____

NUMBER LINES/NEGATIVE NUMBERS

1. **Draw a line from each number to show where it belongs on this number line.**

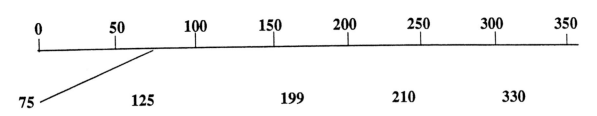

| 0 | 50 | 100 | 150 | 200 | 250 | 300 | 350 |

75   125   199   210   330

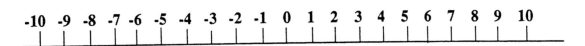

-10 -9 -8 -7 -6 -5 -4 -3 -2 -1 0 1 2 3 4 5 6 7 8 9 10

2. **Use this number line to work out these sums**

3 - 5 = —————   4 - 9 = —————   1 - 7 = —————

3. **At 11 pm the temperature of the water in a tank is 0°C and the water freezes.**

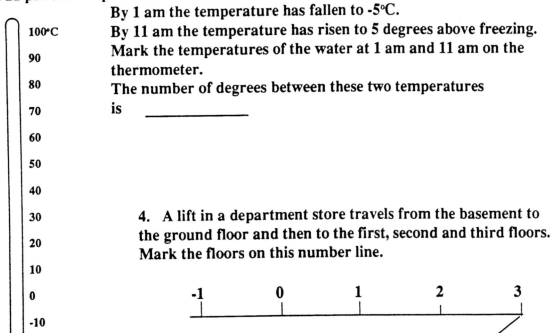

By 1 am the temperature has fallen to -5°C.
By 11 am the temperature has risen to 5 degrees above freezing.
Mark the temperatures of the water at 1 am and 11 am on the thermometer.
The number of degrees between these two temperatures is _____

100°C
90
80
70
60
50
40
30
20
10
0
-10

4. **A lift in a department store travels from the basement to the ground floor and then to the first, second and third floors. Mark the floors on this number line.**

-1   0   1   2   3

Third floor

The lift stops at each floor. How many stops will it make between the basement and the third floor?
The lift makes ————— stops.
How many floors are there between the second floor and the basement?

There are _____ floors.

FUNCTION MACHINES

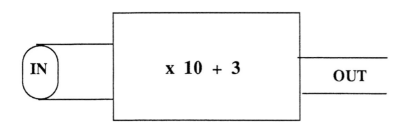

IN	OUT
4	43
7	
	93
11	

Complete this table.

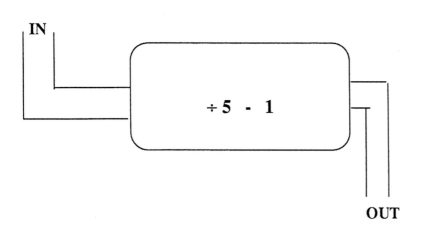

IN	OUT
15	2
30	
	7
45	

Complete this table.

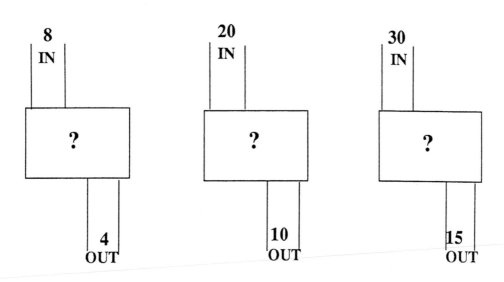

What is this machine doing to each number?

If the numbers 36 and 120 are fed into the machine, the numbers coming out will be

_____ and _____

NUMBERS TO BASE TEN AND TWO

Write the number shown on each abacus. The numbers are to the base ten.

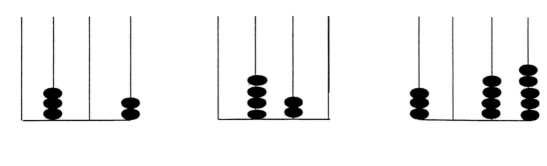

_____   _____   _____

The number 89 written to the base 2 is 1011001. Complete the tables below

	Number to Base Two							Number to Base Ten
128	64	32	16	8	4	2	1	
	1	0	1	1	0	0	1	89
								9
								15
								36
								121

3 is written _____   9 is written _____   15 is written _____

36 is written _____   121 is written _____

Number to Base Two	Number to Base Ten
101	
1111	
10110	

ADDITION AND SUBTRACTION
TENS AND UNITS

Do not use a calculator on this page.

T	U	
1	4	+
2	3	

_____

_____

T	U	
6	2	+
1	0	

_____

_____

T	U	
3	1	+
5	8	

_____

_____

T	U	
7	0	+
2	4	

_____

_____

T	U	
3	8	+
4	9	

_____

_____

T	U	
4	5	+
3	7	

_____

_____

T	U	
2	6	+
1	9	

_____

_____

T	U	
6	3	+
	8	

_____

_____

T	U	
6	3	−
2	2	

_____

_____

T	U	
4	5	−
3	1	

_____

_____

T	U	
7	4	−
5	0	

_____

_____

T	U	
9	3	−
3	2	

_____

_____

T	U	
7	3	−
2	4	

_____

_____

T	U	
6	0	−
4	1	

_____

_____

T	U	
8	1	−
7	2	

_____

_____

T	U	
4	3	−
	9	

_____

_____

Write these figures in columns and work them out.

24 + 36 + 8 + 10

70 + 7 + 42 + 9

27 - 12

34 - 15

50 - 21

64 - 8

87 - 30

ADDITION AND SUBTRACTION
HUNDREDS, TENS AND UNITS

Do not use a calculator on this page.

H	T	U	
1	3	4	
2	8	6	+
3	7	9	

H	T	U	
3	5	7	
1	7	9	+
	9	8	

H	T	U	
3	6	7	
	5	6	+
3	0	5	

H	T	U	
3	0	8	
2	9	9	+
1	2	3	

H	T	U	
4	5	6	_
1	7	5	

H	T	U	
8	9	4	_
6	0	2	

H	T	U	
5	2	0	_
4	2	4	

H	T	U	
6	8	0	_
	4	0	

Write these figures in columns and then work them out.

235 + 157 + 830

5 + 306 + 92

315 - 204

120 - 39

30	5 000	600	9

These numbers add up to 5 639
Add up the following sets of numbers.

300	10	4 000	5	_____

2 000	700	8	80	10 000	_____

41 456 can be written as 40 000 + 1 000 + 400 + 50 + 6

Write the following numbers in the same way.

31 926 _____

78 054 _____

MENTAL ARITHMETIC CARDS

Paste these cards on to a piece of cardboard and cut them out.

58 + 62 =	56 + 23 =	8 x 9 =	35 ÷ 7 =
57 - 28 =	40 - 29 =	4 +3 + 7 =	54 x 8 =
29 + 68 =	20 x 300 =	8 + 6 =	35 + 25 =
7 x 7 =	49 - 25 =	5 + 7 + 3 + 8 =	50 x 60 =
95 ÷ 5 =	66 ÷ 2 =	48 + 12 =	56 - 37 =
98 + 22 =	98 ÷ 2 =	180 ÷ 5 =	221 + 109 =

APPROXIMATE ANSWERS

Work out the approximate answer to each of the following. The first has been done for you.

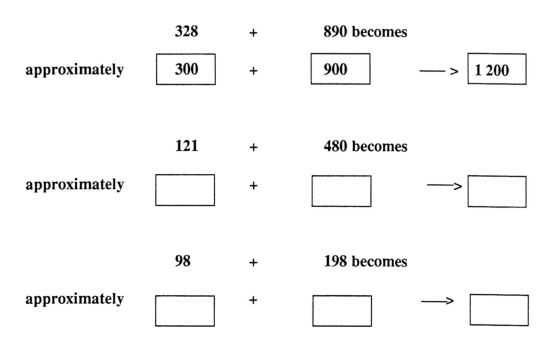

The following represent problems worked out using a calculator. Find the approximate answer before pressing = . The first one has been done for you.

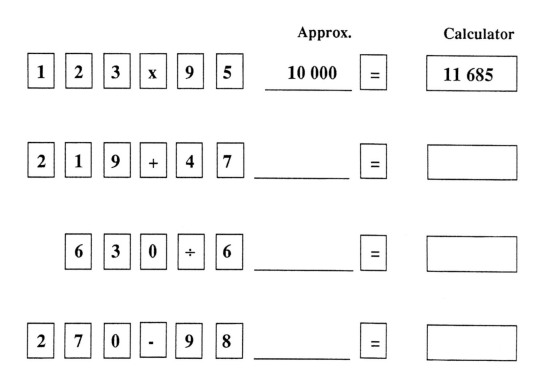

FRACTIONS

What fractions of these figures are shaded?

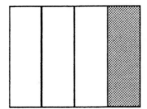   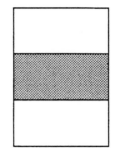   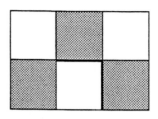

_____   _____   _____

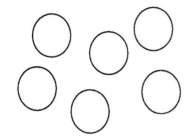

Colour half of these 6 circles.

How many circles have you coloured? _____

Which of these fractions have the same value?

$$\frac{2}{3} \qquad \frac{2}{6} \qquad \frac{5}{10} \qquad \frac{12}{60} \qquad \frac{1}{5} \qquad \frac{2}{8}$$

$$\frac{5}{20} \qquad \frac{4}{20} \qquad \frac{4}{6} \qquad \frac{1}{4} \qquad \frac{1}{3} \qquad \frac{8}{40}$$

$$\frac{2}{4} \qquad \frac{6}{9} \qquad \frac{5}{15} \qquad \frac{3}{12} \qquad \frac{1}{2} \qquad \frac{8}{12}$$

Write these fractions in order of size beginning with the smallest.

$$\frac{1}{3} \qquad \frac{1}{5} \qquad \frac{1}{8} \qquad \frac{1}{6} \qquad \frac{1}{4}$$ _____

PERCENTAGES

1. Write these homework marks as percentages.

$$\frac{45}{100} \qquad \frac{30}{50} \qquad \frac{8}{10} \qquad \frac{15}{20} \qquad \frac{32}{40}$$

_____   _____   _____   _____   _____

2. Write these percentages as fractions.

    30%   25%   60%   75%   90%

_____   _____   _____   _____   _____

3. What percentages of the boxes are shaded?

_____   _____   _____

4. Find 10% of £10   10% of £4   10% of £120   10% of £8.50

_____   _____   _____   _____

5. Find 25% of £8   25% of £12.60   15% of £40   75% of £12.80

_____   _____   _____   _____

6. In a school of 600 pupils, 55% are girls. How many are boys? _____

7. In a group of 50 children, 25 like football, 15 like swimming and 10 do not like sports at all.

_____% like football, _____ % like swimming and _____ % do not like sport.

8. The price of a jacket is £30. In a sale this price is reduced by 25%.

    The sale price is _____

PROBLEMS

You may use a calculator if you wish.

1. The height of a pile of 600 sheets of paper is 6 cm. Calculate
   (i) the thickness of one sheet and (ii) the height of a pile of 320
   sheets.

   1   (i)
       (ii)

2. The height of a pile of 7 boards is 5·6 cm. What is the height of
   a pile of 9 boards?

   2

3. How many 45 seater coaches are needed to carry 305 people?

   3

4. You buy 5 books costing £8·95, £4·30, £6·50, £17·95 and 85p.
   How much change do you receive from two £20 notes?

   4

5. Scores for a cricket team are 3, 42, 0, 6, 18, 100, 9, 12, 18, 14,
   and 20. What is the average score?

   5

6. The classes in a school raise money to buy Christmas hampers
   for the elderly. The amounts collected by the diferent classes
   are £22·50, £19·50, £11·75, £18·55, £23·05 and £17·85.
   Find the average amount collected to the nearest 10p.

   6

7. Three pieces of wood measuring 3·85 cm, 10·60 cm and
   15·25 cm are cut from a piece of wood measuring 1 m.
   What is the length of the piece of wood left?

   7

8. In a race on Sports Day, the following times were recorded:

   Jack   106 sec.
   Jane   110 sec.
   Jim   99 sec.
   Jean   113 sec.

   8

What was the average time for the race?

9. A man earns £12·50 an hour. How long must he work to earn
   £237·50?
   In 5 weeks, he earns £937·50. What are the average number of
   hours he works in a week?

   9

10. A hotel uses 16 *l* of milk on Monday, 15·5 *l* on Tuesday, 18·25 *l*
    on Wednesday, 20 *l* on Thursday and 22 *l* on Friday. What is
    the average amount of milk used on these five days?

   10

MULTIPLICATION AND DIVISION

```
  3  4  8        2  0  6        4  7  9
x    3  2      x    2  9      x    6  7
_____      _____      _____
```

Estimates: 300 x 30 = 900   200 x 30 =

```
         _____              _____              _____
 17 ) 5  9  5        21 ) 3  9  9        38 ) 5  7  0
```

Estimates: 600 ÷ 20 = 30 400 ÷ 20

Do these in your head.

80 x 50 = _____   70 x 40 = _____   700 x 60 = _____

400 ÷ 40 = _____   500 ÷ 20 _____   700 ÷ 50 = _____

The cost of 135 bottles of lemonade @ 19p =
[Estimate

Complete this bill

	£
10 cans of beans @ 37p	3·70
2 loaves of bread @ 39p	
2 litres of milk @ 34p	
2 packets of tea @ £1·75	
8 oz sweets @ 65p per quarter	_____
Total	£

APPROXIMATION

1. Round off the following to the nearest 10.

    22 ——>   148 ——>   385 ——>   205 ——>

2. Round off the following to the nearest 100.

    295 ——>   648 ——>   5849 ——>   3071 ——>

3. Write these numbers correct to one significant figure.

    63 ——>   47 ——>   344 ——>   263 ——>

4. Write these numbers correct to one decimal place.

    3·25 ——>   7·13——>   20·05——>   34·154——>

5. Write these numbers correct to two decimal places.

    45·325——>   9·106 ——>   3·047——>   2·895 ——>

6. In 2 hours Mary puts 186 advertising leaflets into envelopes. Approximately how many leaflets does she put into envelopes in 1 hour?
   Give your answer correct to the nearest 10.   _____

7. A piece of wood 130 cm long is cut into three pieces of equal length. What is the length of each piece?
   Give your answer to 2 significant figures.   _____

8. Detergent is sold in kilogram packets costing £1·55. What is the cost of each wash if 100 g of detergent is used?
   Give your answer correct to the nearest whole pence.   _____

9. A class of 17 children is going to the theatre.
   For the first ten children, the theatre tickets cost £1·80 each. For the next ten children the tickets cost £1·50 each. The ticket for the teacher costs £1·80.
   Calculate the cost of tickets for 17 children and a teacher correct to the nearest £.

                                                          _____

RATIO

1. Draw a plan of your classroom using a ratio of 1:50.

2. This is a plan of the school playground drawn with a scale of 1:1000.

   The shaded area is grass.

   X marks the entrance door to the school.

   Y marks the gates to the playground.

   The length of the playground on the drawing is _____ cm

   The length of the playground is really _____ m

   The distance from X to Y on the diagram is _____ cm

   The distance from X to Y is really_____ m

   The fraction of the playground which is grass is _____

   The percentage of the playground which is grass is _____

3. Robert made a model of his school using a scale factor of 1:50. How high is the door of the model if the door of the school is 2 m? _____

4. Oliver's mother's recipe for cake uses 2 eggs but Oliver only has 1 egg. How must he change the recipe? Complete Oliver's recipe. _____

His mother's cake recipe	Oliver's cake recipe
400 g cooking apples	_____
200 g butter	_____
400 g plain flour	_____
200 g caster sugar	_____
2 eggs	1 egg
3 teaspoons baking powder	

5. Orange squash is to be diluted with water in the ratio 1: 5. How much diluted orange squash can be made from 1 litre of concentrated squash? _____

6. One inch on a map represents fifty miles. If the distance on the map between Birmingham and Cardiff is 2·16 inches, how far is Birmingham from Cardiff?

_____

SQUARE ROOTS AND INDICES

Do not use a calculator on this page.

1. Write the square root of the following:

$\sqrt{9} =$ _____ $\sqrt{16} =$ _____ $\sqrt{36} =$ _____ $\sqrt{49} =$ _____ $\sqrt{64} =$ _____

2. What is the square of the following?

$5^2 =$ _____ $9^2 =$ _____ $10^2 =$ _____ $11^2 =$ _____ $15^2 =$ _____

3. Work out the following.

$4^3 =$ _____ $3^3 =$ _____ $6^3 =$ _____ $2^3 =$ _____ $5^3 =$ _____

$2^5 =$ _____ $10^4 =$ _____ $2^4 =$ _____ $3^4 =$ _____ $10^6 =$ _____

4. Find the areas of these squares.

3 cm

A

Area of square A = _____

4 cm

B

Area of square B = _____

5. The length of a square, Y, is 3 cm. If the length and breadth of the square are doubled, what is the area of the new square, X?

Area of new square X =

Work out the fraction $\dfrac{\text{Area of square X}}{\text{Area of square Y}}$ = _____ = _____

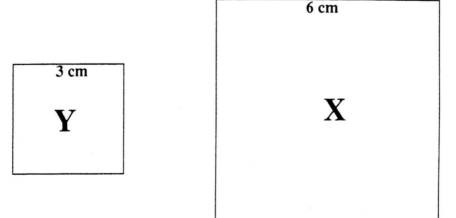

3 cm

Y

6 cm

X

PROBABILITY

1. Join each event to its place on the chance line.

0 = there is no chance it will happen.
1 = it will definitely happen.

0 |_____|_____| 1

| Throw a die to get a one | | Toss a coin to get tails | | Toss a coin to get heads |

2. Join each event to its place on the chance line.

0 = there is no chance it will happen.
1 = it will definitely happen.

0 |_____|_____| 1

| Water freezes when it is heated | | If you stand on one leg, you stand on the left one | | Thunder follows lightning | | Ice floats on water |

3. There are 52 playing cards in a pack. The pack is shuffled and the cards spread over a table, face down.

The chance of turning over a black card is ——————

The chance of turning over a heart card is ——————

The chance of turning over the jack of clubs is ——————

4. There are five toffees and three mints in a bag of sweets. If you put your hand into the bag,

the chance of picking a mint is ——————

the chance of picking a toffee is ——————

UNITS

1.
km	l	kg	years
m	ml	g	months
cm		mg	weeks
mm			days
			hours
			minutes

Which of these units would you choose to measure the following?

The weight of a packet of crisps _____

The thickness of a piece of paper _____

Your age _____

Your height _____

The length of a lesson _____

The length of your foot _____

The volume of petrol in the tank of a car _____

The volume of medicine in a spoon _____

The weight of a tin of baked beans _____

The height of a house _____

2. Calculate

1·3 m = _____ cm   1·5 km = _____ m   3·25 l = _____ ml

3. A spoonful of medicine holds 5 ml. How many spoonfuls can be given from a litre

bottle?   _____

4. A car travels 10 kilometres on a litre of petrol. How far will it travel on 200 ml?

_____

5. A tin of fruit weighs 300 g. Find the weight in kg of 50 tins.

_____

6. A £5 bag of 10 p coins weighs 1 kg. What is the weight of 1 coin in grams?

_____

7. 1 litre is approximately 1·75 pints. How many litre bottles can be filled from a tank

containing 17·5 pints?   _____

8. 10 parcels each have exactly the same weight of 6·5 kg. What is the weight of

1 parcel in grams?   _____

DECIMALS AND FRACTIONS

Do not use a calculator on this page.

1. | 0•05 | + | 0•006 | + | 0•3 | = | |

    | 0•008 | + | 0•09 | + | 0•0004 | + | 0•6 | = | |

    | 1•3 | | +0•5 | + | 0•02 | + | 0•007 | = | |

2. What is the missing decimal?

    | 0•02 | + | | + | 0•8 | = | 0•827 |

3. Change these fractions to decimals.

    $\frac{3}{10}$ = $\frac{1}{2}$ = $\frac{3}{4}$ = $\frac{1}{4}$ =

    $\frac{2}{5}$ = $\frac{3}{20}$ = $\frac{5}{10}$ = $\frac{7}{100}$ =

4. Change these decimals to fractions.

    0•8 =   0•05 =   0•002 =   0•0005 =

5. Map these decimals on this number strip.

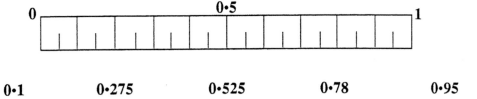

    0•1   0•275   0•525   0•78   0•95

6. Write these fractions as percentages.

    $\frac{3}{10}$ = $\frac{1}{2}$ = $\frac{3}{4}$ = $\frac{1}{4}$ = $\frac{3}{20}$ =

7. Calculate the interest on the following.

    10% interest on £550 = _____   7% interest on £900 = _____

    5% interest on £35 = _____   4% interest on £2 500 = _____

PROBABILITY

1. **Two dice are rolled together. Complete the table below to show the possible total scores.**

	1	2	3	4	5	6
1	2	3	4	5	6	7
2	3	4				
3						
4						
5						
6						

Which total occurs most often? _____

What are the chances of two 2s coming together? _____

2. **The numbers 1 to 10 are written on pieces of card and placed in a bag. If you put your hand in the bag, the chances of picking the number 1 out of the bag is**

_____

3. **The letters in the word MATHEMATICS are printed on cards and the cards placed in a bag. If you put your hand in the bag, the chances of picking**

the letter E = _____   the letter M = _____

the letter B = _____

4. **A box contains 4 red counters and 1 white counter.**

The chance of picking the white counter is _____

The chance of not picking the white counter is _____

5. **A die in the form of an octahedron (it has eight faces) has its faces numbered 1, 2, 3, 3, 4, 5, 5, 6. When the die is thrown, the score is taken from the face on which the die lands. The probability of obtaining**

a score of 6 = _____   a score of 3 = _____

MISSING NUMBERS AND SYMBOLS

1. What must be added to these numbers to make 10? The first has been done for you.

| 10 | + 0 = 10 | | + 1 = 10 | | + 2 = 10 | | + 3 = 10 | | + 4 = 10 |

| | + 5 = 10 | | + 6 = 10 | | + 7 = 10 | | + 8 = 10 | | + 9 = 10 |

2. Put a circle around the even numbers and a square around the odd numbers.

3,   14,   23,   7,   31,   12,   8,   19,   33,   22,

1,   4,   25,   18,   6,   10,   2,   5,   36,   21

3. These are some of the numbers which add up to 5

5 = 5 + 0   5 = 4 + 1   5 = 3 + 2   5 = 3 + 1 + 1   5 = 2 + 2 + 1

Write seven combinations which add up to 7. One has been done for you.

7 = _____   7 = _____   7 = _____   7 = _____

7 = 2 + 2 + 3   7 = _____   7 = _____

4. Suggest numbers to take the place of the symbols * and † in the following. The first has been done for you.

* + 2 = 6   * + 4 = 7   3 + † = 9   5 + † = 8   * + 6 = 10

* = 4   * = ___   † = ___   † = ___   * = ___

† - 3 = 8   * - 4 = 5   8 - † = 2   9 - † = 7   6 - * = 3

† = ___   * = ___   † = ___   † = ___   * = ___

NUMBER PATTERNS

1. Find the patterns and the next three numbers in each series.

1,	4,	7,	10,	_____
10,	20,	30,	40,	_____
2,	4,	8,	16,	_____
33,	31,	29,	27,	_____
0,	5,	10,	15,	_____
28,	24,	20,	16,	_____
$\frac{1}{2}$,	$\frac{1}{3}$,	$\frac{1}{4}$,	$\frac{1}{5}$,	_____

2. Which of the following numbers are exactly divisible by 2 or by 5 or by 10?

1, 5, 6, 9, 10, 12, 13, 15, 16, 17, 20, 21, 22, 23, 25, 26, 27, 30

Numbers divisible by 2 are _____

Numbers divisible by 5 are _____

Numbers divisible by 10 are _____

Complete the Venn diagram.

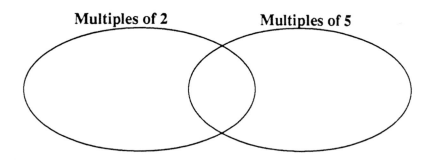

Multiples of 2   Multiples of 5

3. When the operation arrow is reversed, the operation changes. For example

$$3 \xrightarrow{(\text{x } 2 \text{ -1})} 5 \qquad \text{becomes} \qquad 3 \xleftarrow{(+ 1 \div 2)} 5$$

Write the new operations on these arrows.

$$4 \xrightarrow{(-1 \text{ x } 2)} 6 \qquad 8 \xrightarrow{(\div 2 \text{ x } 3)} 12 \qquad 15 \xrightarrow{(\div 5 + 4)} 7$$

$$4 \xleftarrow{\hspace{2cm}} 6 \qquad 8 \xleftarrow{\hspace{2cm}} 12 \qquad 15 \xleftarrow{\hspace{2cm}} 7$$

FUNCTION MACHINES

1. **This is an add 3 machine. Find the numbers that come out of it.**

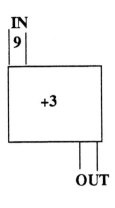 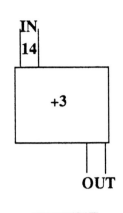 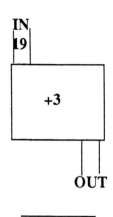

2. **If 17 and 25 came out of this machine, what numbers went in?**

_____ **and** _____

3. **I double a number then add 5. The answer is 17.**
   The number is _____

   I halve a number then take away 4. The answer is 6.
   The number is _____

4.

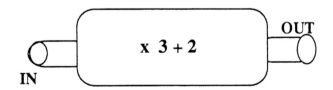

Complete this table.

IN	OUT
4	14
1	
5	
9	
	20
	32

5. **Write in words what happens to the numbers fed into the machine.**

   The machine_____ **and then**

   _____

ADDITION AND
MULTIPLICATION SQUARES

1. Complete these addition squares.

+	1	2	3	4
1				
2				
3				
4				

+	2	4	6	8
2				
4				
6				
8				

+	2	5	10	15
2				
5				
10				
15				

+	10	20	30	40
10				
20				
30				
40				

2. Complete these multiplication squares.

X	1	2	3	4
1				
2				
3				
4				

X	2	4	6	8
2				
4				
6				
8				

X	5	10	15	20
5				
10				
15				
20				

X	3	5	7	9
3				
5				
7				
9				

CO-ORDINATES

1. Write the co-ordinates of each letter.

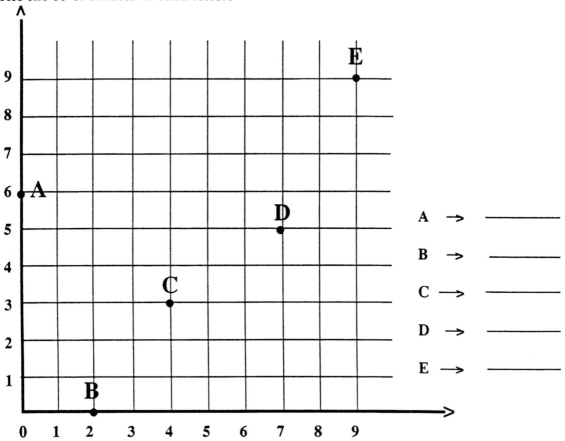

A → ——————

B → ——————

C → ——————

D → ——————

E → ——————

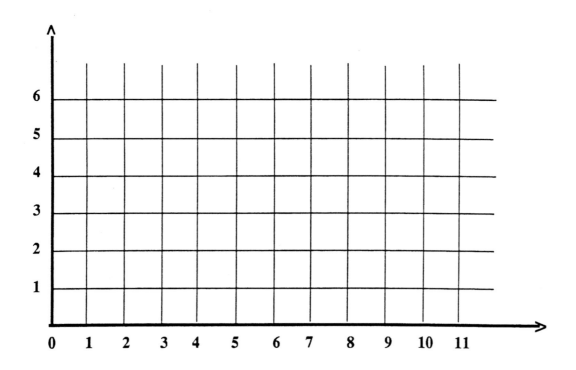

Plot these points.

A (3, 2)   B (8, 2)   C (8, 5)   D (3, 5)   E (4, 6)   F (7, 6)

Join the points to make a house.

PRIME NUMBERS AND MULTIPLES

1. Look at the hundred number square.

Put a circle around 1.

Put a circle around all the multiples of 2 except 2.

Put a circle around all the multiples of 3 except 3.

Put a circle around all the multiples of 5 except 5.

Put a circle around all the multiples of 7 except 7.

1	2	3	4	5	6	7	8	9	10
11	12	13	14	15	16	17	18	19	20
21	22	23	24	25	26	27	28	29	30
31	32	33	34	35	36	37	38	39	40
41	42	43	44	45	46	47	48	49	50
51	52	53	54	55	56	57	58	59	60
61	62	63	64	65	66	67	68	69	70
71	72	73	74	75	76	77	78	79	80
81	82	83	84	85	86	87	88	89	90
91	92	93	94	95	96	97	98	99	100

Write the numbers not circled.

_____

_____

_____

The numbers you have written are called _____

2. $6^3 = 6 \times 6 \times 6 = 216$ Work out the following

$2^2 =$ _____ $3^2 =$ _____ $4^2 =$ _____ $5^2 =$ _____

$2^3 =$ _____ $3^3 =$ _____ $4^3 =$ _____ $5^3 =$ _____

$2^4 =$ _____ $3^4 =$ _____ $9^2 =$ _____ $11^2 =$ _____

3. $\sqrt{4} =$ _____ $\sqrt{16} =$ _____ $\sqrt{25} =$ _____ $\sqrt{36} =$ _____

$\sqrt{81} =$ _____ $\sqrt{100} =$ _____ $\sqrt{10\,000} =$ _____ $\sqrt[3]{8} =$ _____

$\sqrt[3]{27} =$ _____ $\sqrt[3]{64} =$ _____ $\sqrt[3]{125} =$ _____ $\sqrt[4]{16} =$ _____

EQUIVALENT FRACTIONS

A   **B**   **C**   **D**

1. In A, 3 out of 4 squares are shaded. The fraction shaded = $\frac{3}{4}$.

   In B, 6 out of 8 sections are shaded. The fraction shaded = $\frac{6}{8}$ = $\frac{3}{4}$.

   $\frac{3}{4}$ and $\frac{6}{8}$ are equivalent fractions.

   Shade $\frac{3}{4}$ of C. The number of sections shaded = _____

   Shade $\frac{3}{4}$ of D. The number of sections shaded = _____

2. Find the missing numbers.

$$\frac{1}{2} = \frac{2}{\square} = \frac{3}{\square} = \frac{\square}{8} = \frac{\square}{10} = \frac{\square}{12}$$

$$\frac{1}{4} = \frac{2}{\square} = \frac{\square}{12} = \frac{4}{\square} = \frac{\square}{20} = \frac{6}{\square}$$

$$\frac{2}{5} = \frac{4}{\square} = \frac{6}{\square} = \frac{\square}{20} = \frac{10}{\square} = \frac{\square}{30}$$

FLOWCHARTS AND FUNCTION PROBLEMS

1. Flowcharts change numbers and also help you to solve problems.

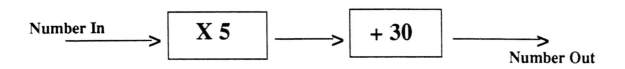

Number In ⟶ | **X 5** | ⟶ | **+ 30** | ⟶

Number Out

This flowchart could be the formula for calculating wages.

Suppose wages (in £) are calculated by multiplying the number of hours worked by 5 and then adding 30.

From the table, if you worked for 20 hours, your wages would be £130.   [5 x 20 and + 30]

Complete the table

IN	OUT
20	130
30	
	255

Wages for working 30 hours = _____

Nunber of hours worked to earn £255 = _____

Find the values of y in these function problems. The first one has been done for you.

1.   y = x + 2

   If x = 4   y = 6

   If x = 7   y =

   If x = 20   y =

2.   y = 3x

   If x = 6   y =

   If x = 12   y =

   If x = 21   y =

3. $y = \dfrac{x}{2}$

   If x = 4   y =

   If x = 9   y =

   If x = 32   y =

4.   y = 2x + 3

   If x = 3   y =

   If x = 7   y =

   If x = 9   y =

PROBLEMS

1. The cost of n cakes when 1 cake costs c pence = _____

2. If 1 sweet has a mass of m g, the mass of s sweets = _____

3. Two cricketers score a total of 80 runs.
   If one scores R runs, the other scores _____ runs.

4. Three pieces of wood each N cm long are cut from a piece of wood 1 m long.
   The length of the wood left = _____

5. Three cups each holding 150 ml are filled from a litre bottle of water.
   How much water is left in the bottle? _____

6. How many stamps can be bought with £1 if each costs 23p? _____

7. The cost of a pot of tea in a café is calculated using the formula

$$C = 40 + 30n$$

   where C is the price (in pence) charged and n is the number of teabags put in the pot.

   The cost of a pot when 5 teabags are used = _____

8. Car expenses for journeys are paid at 25p per mile plus 50p. Write this information into the flowchart below and complete the table below.

Number In $\longrightarrow$ (X) $\longrightarrow$ (+) $\longrightarrow$ Number Out

Give your answers in £

Complete the table.

IN	OUT
5	175
10	
	550

The expenses for a journey of 5 miles = _____

The expenses for a journey of 10 miles = _____

When the expenses are £5.50, the journey = _____

Write the formula for calculating the expenses

_____

CO - ORDINATES

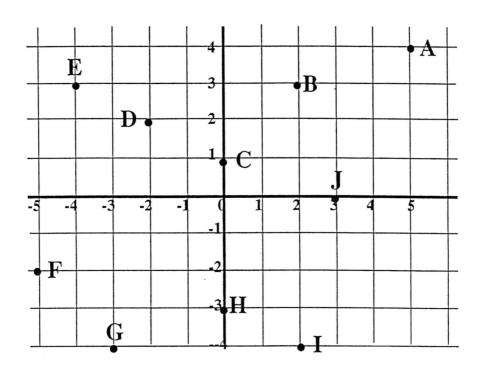

1. Write the co-ordinates of the points A to J

   A (5,4)   B   C   D   E
   _____

   F   G   H   I   J
   _____

2. Plot these points

   K(1,2)   L(4,1)   M(5,0)   N(4,-2)   O(1,-3)

   P(0,-2)   Q(-1,-1)   R(-4,0)   S(-3,4)   T(0,3)

3. This is a plan showing where the children sit in the classroom.

   The number of children in the class is _____

   | | | FRONT | | |

   (grid rows 1, 2, 3, 4 and columns A B C D E F)

   Jack Smith sits in the square D2 and his friend, Alan sits behind him.

   Alan sits in square _____

   Jane sits in the square F2 and her friend, Helen, sits to the left of her

   Helen sits in square _____

Two boys who misbehave when they sit together have to sit as far apart as possible in the front row. Where do they sit? _____ and _____

GRAPHS

1. Plot the graph of y = 2x + 1.
   Complete the table to work out the points to plot.

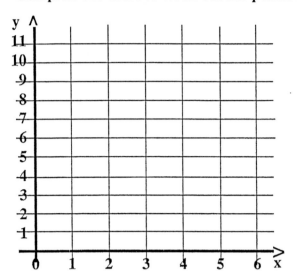

x	0	1	2
2x	0	2	
+1	1		
y	1		

Use your graph to find the value of y when x = 4 and the value of x when y = 11

When x = 4, y = _____   When y = 11, x = _____

2. Plot the graph of y = x² using the values of x and y in the box.
   Some of the points have been plotted for you.

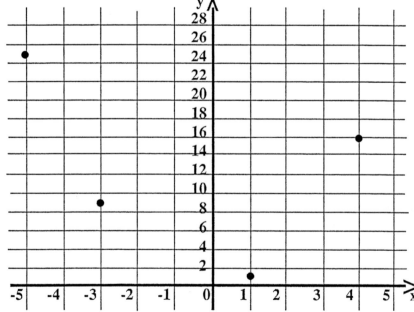

x	y
-5	25
-4	16
-3	9
-2	4
-1	1
0	0
1	1
2	4
3	9
4	16
5	25

From the graph find the value of x when y = 12. Hence find √12.
Compare your answer with that using a calculator (to 1 dec. pl.)
Complete the following.

When y = 12

x = _____

From graph	Calculator answer to 1 dec. pl.
√8 =	
√14 =	
√20 =	

√12 = _____

EQUATIONS

1. Solve these equations.

$3x + 2 = 14$

$20 - 4m = 8$

x = _____

m = _____

$7p + 1 = 15$

$4t - 2 = 2t + 4$

p = _____

t = _____

$8z - 10 = 30$

$5s + 6 = 10s - 14$

z = _____

s = _____

$9y - 6 = 39$

$2h - 2 = 3h - 4$

y = _____

h = _____

2. The length of a rectangle is 5 cm longer than its breadth . If its perimeter is 42 cm, write an equation and find the length and breadth.

Length = _____   Breadth = _____

3. There are 10 more toffees than hard boiled sweets in a bag. If there are 24 sweets in the bag, write an equation and find the number of toffees.

Number of toffees = _____

4. When a number (n) is doubled and 5 added to it the answer is the same as if the number had been multiplied by 3. Write an equation and find the number.

Number = _____

5. A boy eats 3 sandwiches for every 2 eaten by his sister. At tea they eat 10 sandwiches. Write an equation and find the number of sandwiches eaten by the girl.

Number of sandwiches eaten by girl = _____

SHAPES

1. Join each shape to its name.

Cube

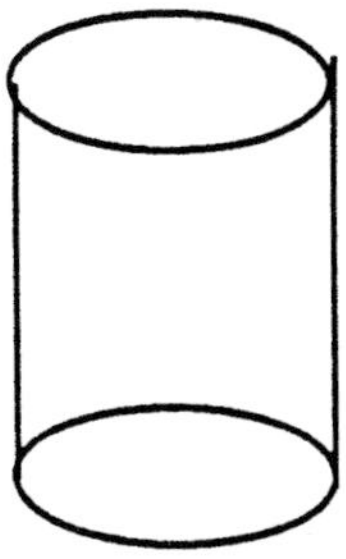

Circle

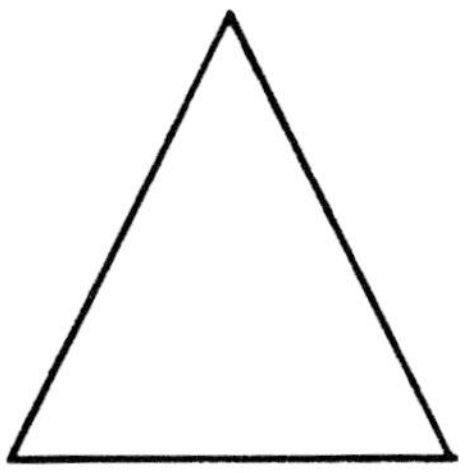

Cylinder

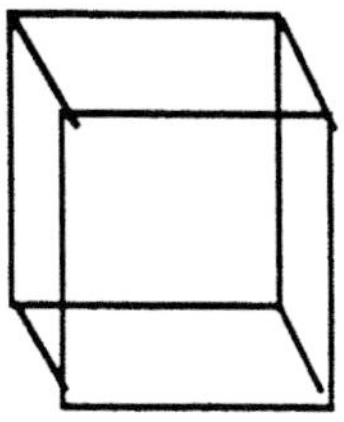

Cuboid

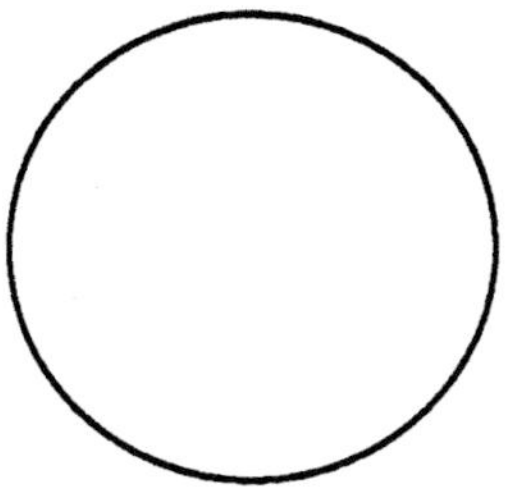

Square

Oval

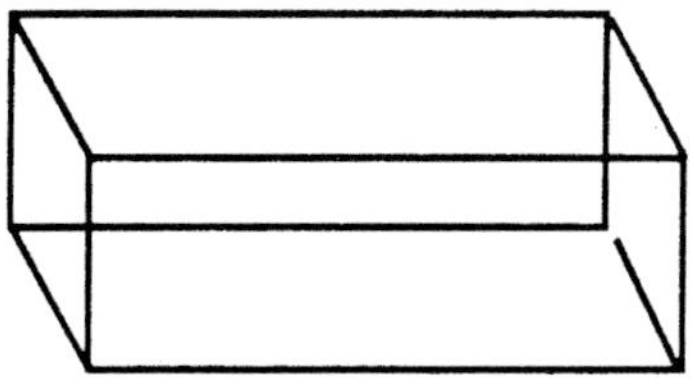

Triangle

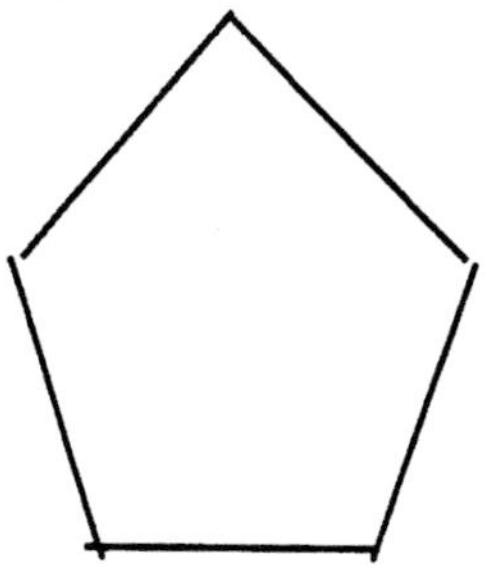

Hexagon

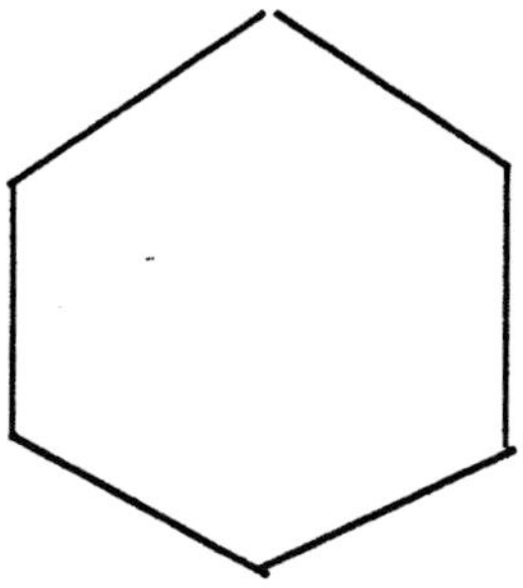

Rectangle

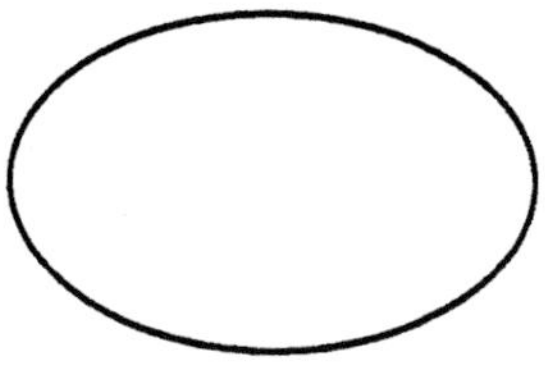

Pentagon

QUADRILATERALS

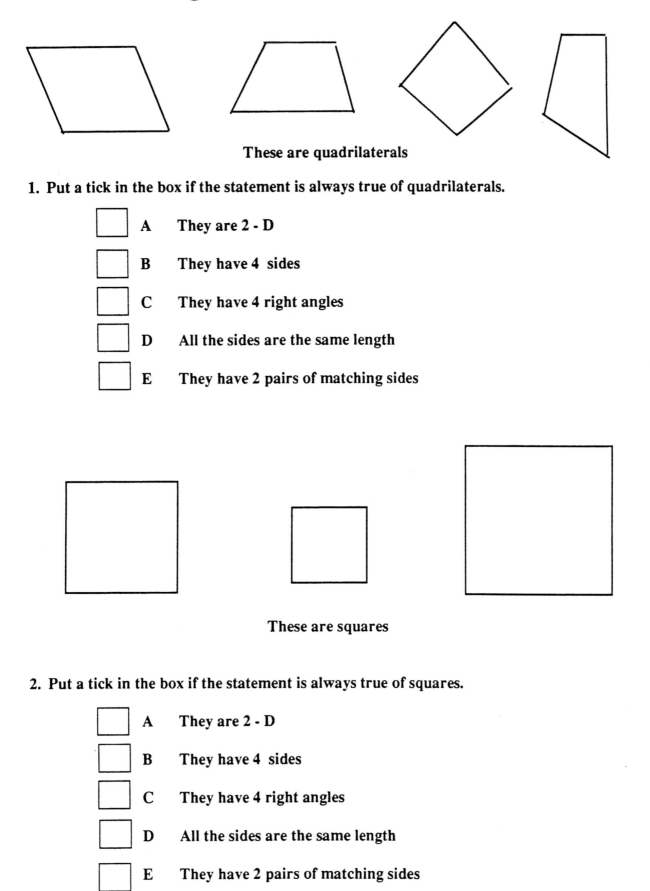

These are quadrilaterals

1. **Put a tick in the box if the statement is always true of quadrilaterals.**

   ☐ A   They are 2 - D

   ☐ B   They have 4 sides

   ☐ C   They have 4 right angles

   ☐ D   All the sides are the same length

   ☐ E   They have 2 pairs of matching sides

These are squares

2. **Put a tick in the box if the statement is always true of squares.**

   ☐ A   They are 2 - D

   ☐ B   They have 4 sides

   ☐ C   They have 4 right angles

   ☐ D   All the sides are the same length

   ☐ E   They have 2 pairs of matching sides

RECTANGLES AND SQUARES

These are rectangles

1. **Put a tick in the box if the statement is always true of rectangles.**

- [ ] A   They are 2 - D
- [ ] B   They have 4 sides
- [ ] C   They have 4 right angles
- [ ] D   All the sides are the same length
- [ ] E   They have 2 pairs of matching sides

Remember, rectangles are 'special' quadrilaterals and squares are 'special' rectangles.

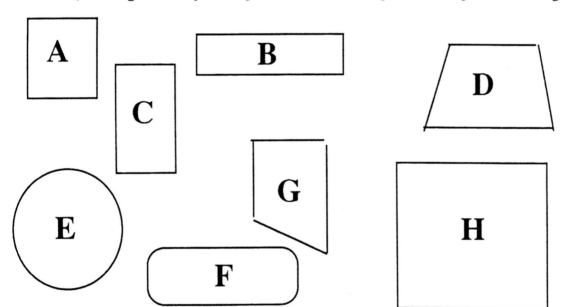

2. **List these under the following headings**

Rectangle	Square	Quadrilateral but not a rectangle or square	Not a quadrilateral

RIGHT ANGLES

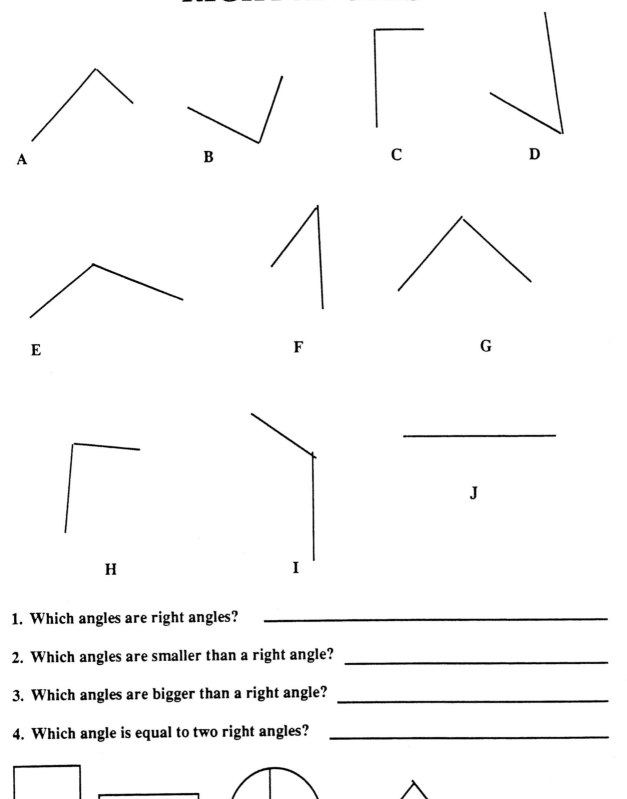

1. Which angles are right angles? _____

2. Which angles are smaller than a right angle? _____

3. Which angles are bigger than a right angle? _____

4. Which angle is equal to two right angles? _____

5. Mark all the angles in the figures which are right angles.

SORTING

1. Find the odd one out in each group.

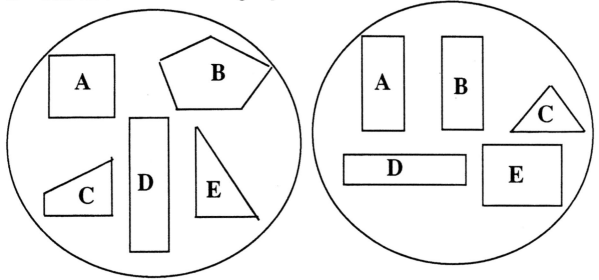

The odd one out is _____   The odd one out is _____

because _____   because _____

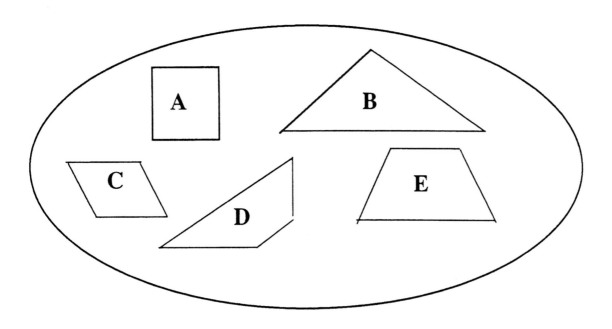

The odd one out is _____

because _____

SIMILARITY AND CONGRUENCY

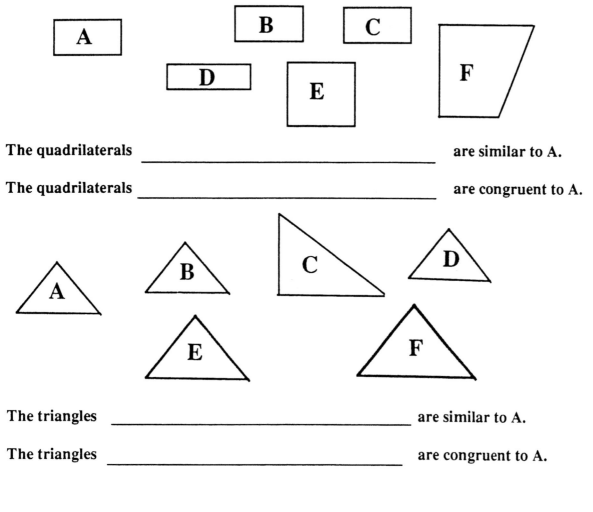

The quadrilaterals _____ are similar to A.

The quadrilaterals _____ are congruent to A.

The triangles _____ are similar to A.

The triangles _____ are congruent to A.

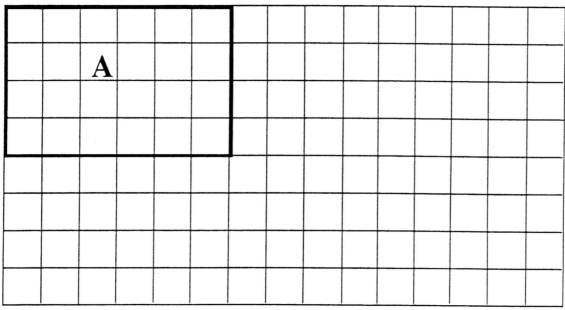

Draw a rectangle which is congruent to A and label it X then draw a rectangle which is similar to A and label it Y.

TOWN MAP

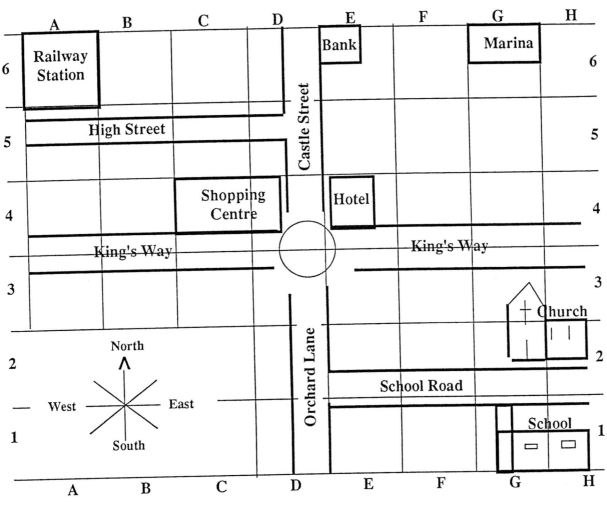

Name the rest of the points of the compass on the map.

Follow the examples that have been done for you.

The school is located in squares G1, H1.

The shopping centre is located in squares _____

The railway station is located in square _____

The shopping centre is south east of the railway station.

The bank is _____ of the hotel.

The marina is _____ of the hotel.

Draw these buildings on the map.

The museum in square G4   The library in square E2

The leisure centre in square C6   The castle in square E5

Tell a visitor to the town how to reach the hotel from the station.

_____

SYMMETRY

1. Make these shapes look the same each side of the dotted line.

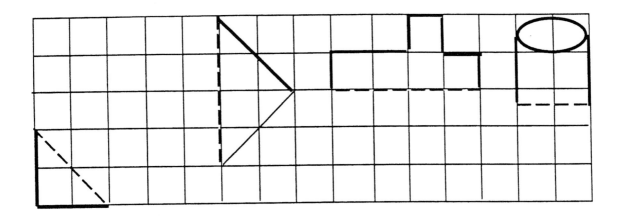

The dotted lines are _____

2. Draw all the lines of symmetry on these shapes. Write the number of lines of symmetry under each one.

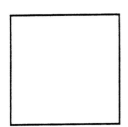   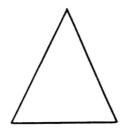   

_____   _____   _____

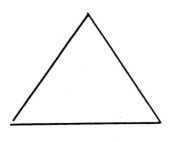   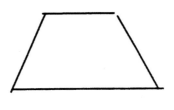   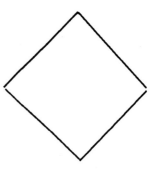

_____   _____   _____

SYMMETRY

1. Which of these shapes have rotational symmetry?

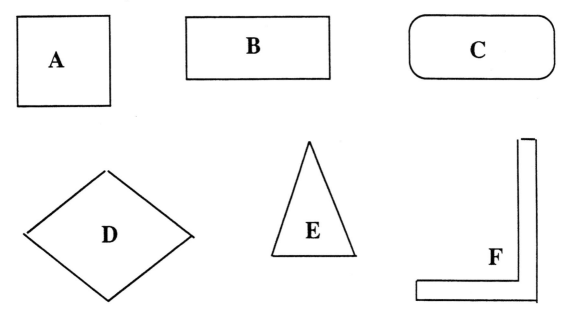

Shapes with rotational symmetry are ———————————————————————

2. Which of these letters have rotational symmetry?

M   L

A   X

T   H   S

Letters with rotational symmetry are ———————————————————————

AREAS AND PERIMETERS

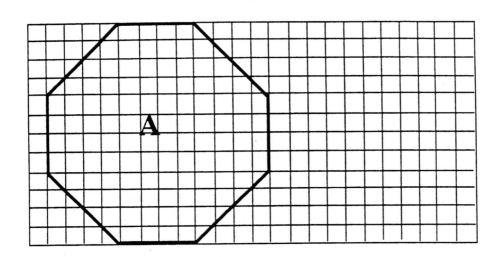

1. Count the number of squares in the octagon A and so find its area.
   Draw an octagon with sides equal to half those of A. Label your octagon B.

   Count the number of squares in B and so find its area.

   Area of A = _____ squares   Area of B = _____ squares

   Ratio $\dfrac{\text{Area A}}{\text{Area B}}$ = _____ = _____

   To draw B, the length of the sides of A have been halved. Write in words how the area of B compares with the area of A.

   _____

2. Find the perimeters of the following figures.

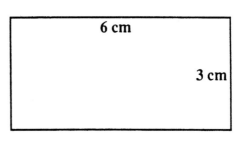

   _____   _____

3. Calculate the perimeter of a rectangle length 5 cm, width 2 cm.   _____

4. Calculate the length of a rectangle if its perimeter is 12 cm and its length is twice its width.

   _____

AREAS

Remember the area of a rectangle is length x breadth, for a square length = breadth.
The area of a triangle is $\frac{1}{2}$ base x perpendicular height.

Complete this table.

RECTANGLES LENGTH	BREADTH	AREA
12 cm	20 cm	
	35 cm	140 cm²
29·5 cm	13·75 cm	
8 in	4·5 in	
65 ft		1755 ft²

SQUARES LENGTH	BREADTH	AREA
		625 cm²
		900 cm²
		20·25 ft²
		39·69 in²

TRIANGLES BASE	PERPENDICULAR HEIGHT	AREA
12 cm	15 cm	
	25 cm	187·5 cm²
40 mm		600 mm²
2·6 in	5 in	
8 ft		100 ft²

CIRCLES AND CUBES

1. The area of a circle is πr^2 where r is the radius of the circle and $\pi = \frac{22}{7}$.
    Find the area of these circles.

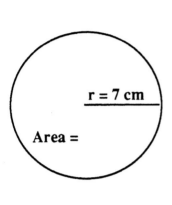

r = 7 cm

Area =

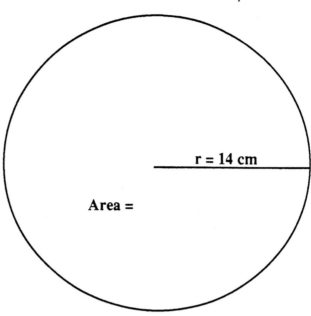

r = 14 cm

Area =

What happens to the area of a circle when the radius is doubled?

_____

2. Find the radius and diameter of a circle of area 1386 cm². ($\pi = \frac{22}{7}$)

    Radius = _____   Diameter = _____

3.

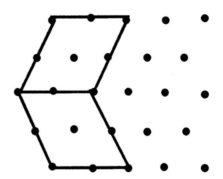

Complete this drawing of a cube and find its volume.

                                        Volume = _____

TESSELLATIONS AND NETWORKS

1. The diagram below shows two triangular tiles. Colour one tile red and the other blue. Use paper with 1 cm dots to find out what patterns you can make with them.

John wants to use tiles like these to cover a bathroom wall 3 metres long by 4 metres high. The tiles can be of one or more colours and can include some tiles with special 'bathroom designs' on them. There are many possible patterns to make by arranging the colours in different ways. When two of the tiles are placed together, they make a square of side 10 cm. Make a plan of the tiling using paper with dots 1 cm apart.
Make a list of the number of each kind needed. If the triangular tiles cost 99p each and the 'bathroom design' ones cost £1.50 each, find the total cost of the tiles you have used in your plan.

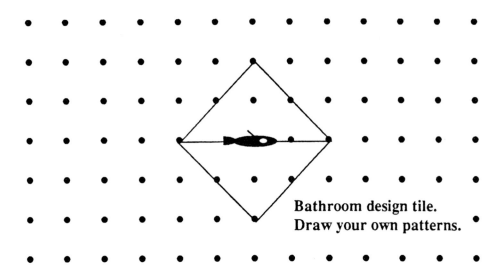

Bathroom design tile.
Draw your own patterns.

2. Which of these can be traversed?

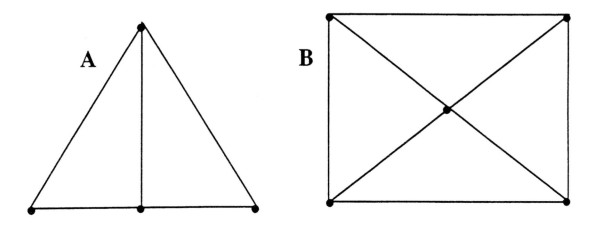

A

B

TALLY AND FREQUENCY CHARTS

1. **In January it rained on 4 Mondays, 3 Tuesdays, 1 Wednesday, 3 Fridays, 2 Saturdays and 1 Sunday.**
   Record this information as a Weather Tally Chart

	Tally	Frequency
Mondays	/ / / /	4
Tuesdays	/ / /	3
Wednesdays	/	1
Thursdays		0
Fridays	/ / /	3
Saturdays	/ /	2
Sundays	/	1

On how many days did it rain?

_____

On how many days did it not rain?

_____

Which day of the week was the wettest?

_____

The Explorers' Club meets on Saturday morning when it is fine. How often did it have to cancel its meetings?

_____

Using a small umbrella to represent rain, record the rainy days in the following chart. Mondays have been done for you.

Mondays

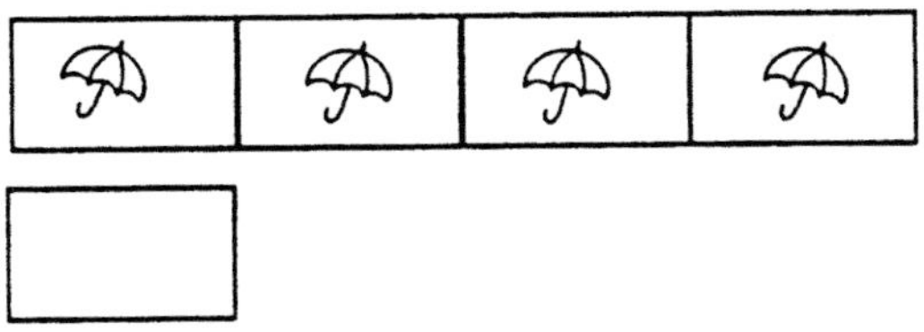

Tuesdays

Wednesdays

Thursdays

Fridays

Saturdays

Sundays

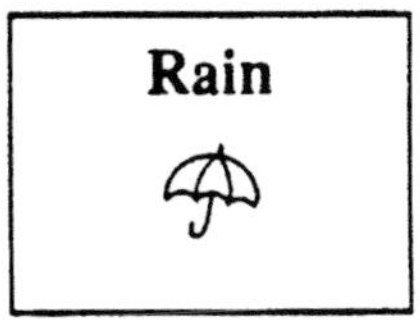

Rain

LISTS AND TABLES

1. List the following under 3 headings.

Jennifer Edward Art   Geography   Science   John   Elsie

Margaret   Paul   Computer Studies   Colin   Joanne

Derek   Music   PE   Richard   Jane   Gareth

Sarah Nature Study   Raymond   Maths   Cookery

Rose   Charles   Elizabeth   History

Suggested headings

Boys in my class	Girls in my class	Lessons

2. Make a shopping list for the family weekly visit to the supermarket.
   Which items are bought every week and which are bought occasionally?

Every week _____

_____

Occasionally _____

3. 20 children were asked to name their two favourite kinds of television programmes.
   4 said they liked pop music and nature programmes, 6 liked pop music and sport,
   8 liked horror films and sport, 2 said they liked sport and nature programmes.
   Make a table of this information.

How many liked horror films? _____

Which was the most popular kind of programme? _____

Which was the least popular kind of programme? _____

BAR CHARTS

These are the numbers of packets of different kinds of crisps sold in the school shop.

Monday - 3 smokey bacon, 6 plain, 8 salt and vinegar, 4 onion.
Tuesday - 2 smokey bacon, 4 plain, 6 salt and vinegar, 2 onion.
Wednesday - 5 smokey bacon, 3 plain, 2 salt and vinegar, 2 onion.
Thursday - 3 smokey bacon, 5 plain, 6 salt and vinegar, 3 onion.
Friday - 7 smokey bacon, 7 plain, 8 salt and vinegar, 3 onion.

Record this information in columns.

Kind of Crisps	Smokey Bacon	Plain	Salt and Vinegar	Onion
Monday	3	6	8	4
Tuesday				

Make a bar chart to show the number of packets of different kinds of crisps sold in a week

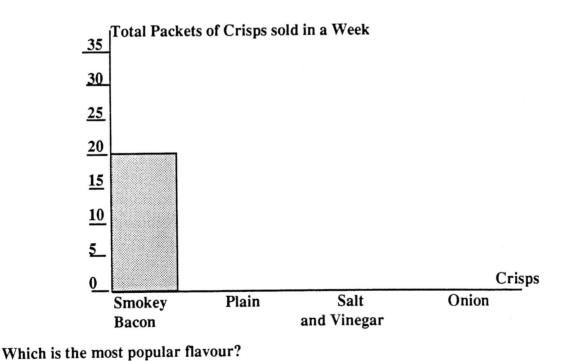

Which is the most popular flavour? _____

Which is the least popular flavour? _____

How many packets are sold in a week? _____

INFORMATION AND ANALYSIS

1. This is the timetable for trains travelling between Garnet and Bearsville in the morning.

Depart Garnet	Arrive Snaptown	Arrive Bearsville
7.00	7.20	7.45
8.00	8.20	8.45
9.00	9.20	9.45

How long is the journey from Garnet to Bearsville? _____

How long is the journey from Snaptown to Bearsville? _____

At what time does the 8.00 am train from Garnet arrive at Bearsville? _____

The return train in the evening which leaves Bearsville at 5.30 pm will arrive at Garnet at _____

2. This is a bar graph of the height of children in a school

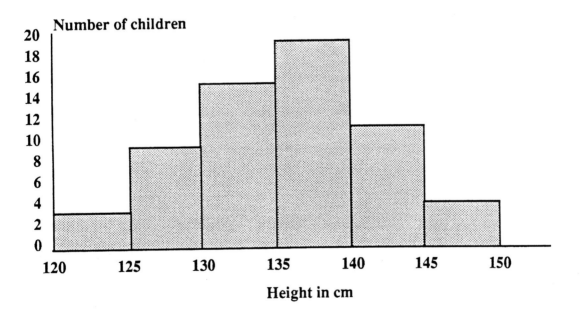

How many children are between 135 and 140 cm tall? _____

How many children are shorter than 135 cm? _____

How many children are taller than 140 cm? _____

How many children were measured? _____

INFORMATION AND ANALYSIS

1. Parents concerned about the traffic travelling through the one way system past the school measure the traffic each morning between 8.30 am and 9.00 am. On average they find 100 vehicles pass point A at this time each morning.

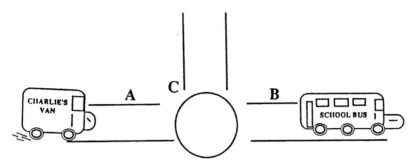

Traffic passing A may turn at C or continue on to B. No traffic joins the system at C.

Complete this Traffic Table.

Vehicles passing A	Vehicles passing C	Vehicles passing B
80 cars		60 cars
15 lorries	4 lorries	
5 buses	1 buses	

How many cars turn off to C? _____   How many lorries pass B? _____

What percentage of the traffic passing B consists of lorries and buses? _____

2.

Cocoa beans are used to make the best chocolate if they are given over 20 points in a series of quality tests. Each of the five beans above represents 1 tonne and their quality is shown by the numbers on the markers.

What percentage of the beans can be used to make chocolate?

_____

If all the beans could be used the farmer would sell his crop for £1 000 per tonne but he cannot sell the beans that do not reach the required standard.
What price per tonne must he ask if he is to get the same money he would have received if all the beans were acceptable?

_____

GRAPHS AND PIE CHARTS

1.

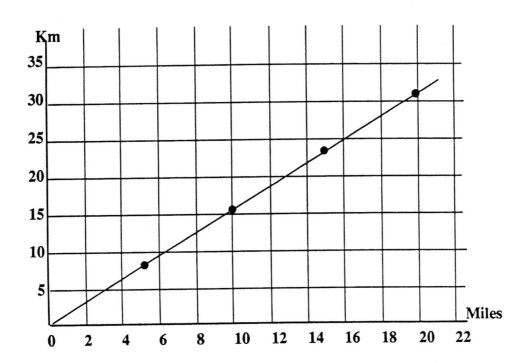

Use the graph of miles/kilometres to complete the following.

	8		16		miles
5		20		30	km

2.

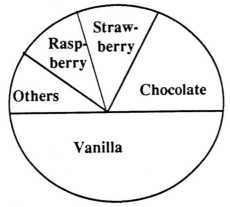

This pie chart shows the ice cream children like.

Which is the favourite ice cream? _____

Which is the second favourite ice cream? _____

Which two flavours are about equally popular? _____

SCATTER GRAPH

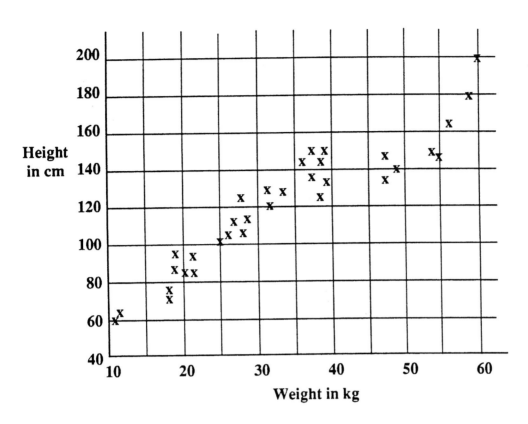

This is a graph showing the weight and height of several children. Each x represents the weight and height of one child.

What is the weight of a child of height 140 cm likely to be?

Between _____

What is the height of a child weighing 27·5 kg likely to be?

Between _____

How many children weigh less than 30 kg? _____

How many children are taller than 140 cm? _____

How many children were weighed and measured? _____

Draw the 'best line' between the crosses.

Not all the crosses will fall exactly on this line. Why is this?

_____

Prepare a similar graph for your class.

TEACHERS' NOTES
AND RESOURCES

Mathematics is part of our daily lives: shopping, cooking, sewing, building, almost everything is measured and calculated. Time, cost, mass, the list is endless. All too often we hear 'I'm no good at maths. I hated the subject at school.'

Fortunately, most of us are better at mathematics than we think. We juggle complicated facts and figures, make split second estimates and decisions and mostly do very well. We link gallons of petrol, fuel consumption, miles and time for journeys, we cope with railway timetables and schedules, we understand codes like traffic lights, we calculate exchange rates for holidays, cope with decimalisation and a mix of metric and imperial units. Confusion and fear arise when this mass of material is unfamiliar.

When we meet a new situation we immediately apply our personal experience to deal with it. If necessary we experiment and extend information we have stored mentally until we can cope. Children, especially young ones, soak up information like blotting paper. Everything is a challenge and one of the joys of teaching is seeing children grow in confidence.

The early years of learning the subject are perhaps the most important in the development of mathematical ability. It is at this stage that children become interested or bored, love the subject or hate it and above all become confident or confused and fearful of mathematical material. For example, failure to develop good spacial awareness may cause problems later in advanced disciplines such as engineering, craft, design and technology. It is often girls who lose out when they are little. They should be encouraged to play with teaching aids such as Lego just as the boys need to be encouraged to take part in cooking experiments.

It is important to begin teaching a new topic within the child's experience. Build on this and gradually extend it. Always start with material the child can handle confidently. Go back to earlier work and the security of familiar ground. Sometimes extra time for play is needed. Never allow a child to stay confused or worried.

Mathematics is best taught in context whenever possible. It should be practical. The drawing of a block of wood does not convey the reality of holding it in the hand, feeling the warmth, the texture and its hardness, looking at the colour or natural patterns of the grain, smelling the paint or natural scents. Young children learn best when things have a reality that they can touch, feel and hold.

Mathematics should be fun. There is much to talk about, new words to learn, experiments, games and puzzles to try. At all times link what is taught with experiences outside the classroom, in the 'real' world, with 'real' work.

Children love to see their work displayed. Sometimes it can go home to show to parents, who hopefully will appreciate its importance. As much as possible should be displayed in the classroom. It should be possible for everyone's work to be shown at some time. Displays should have clear headings so that everyone knows what they are about. Encourage children to draw pictures and later diagrams to illustrate their work.

Life is all about problem solving and so is mathematics. Children love to find solutions and have more satisfaction from their own results than from other people's. Problem solving also develops social skills, especially when they work in groups.

Children have to learn to work together, co-operate with each other, to listen to the ideas of others and offer suggestions of their own.

Children have to develop strategies, experiment and try out ideas, test theories and modify them.

They have to use skills learned and concepts acquired within the context of the problem to be solved. This helps to reinforce the usefulness of what they have learned.

NUMBER
LEVELS 2 - 6

EARLY COUNTING

Children become familiar with numbers when they are very small. They know which toys and how many are theirs, what is their fair share of sweets or other goodies. Here they are probably matching sets rather than counting or using numbers.

Chanting, for example

1, 2, 3, 4, 5
Once I caught a fish alive
6, 7, 8, 9, 10
Then I let it go again

does not ensure that the child actually has any concept of what the numbers mean.

The teaching of number begins with things children are familiar with - 1 hat, 1 coat, 1 desk, 1 chair, 2 shoes, 2 hands, 2 gloves, 2 eyes, 4 fingers and a thumb on each hand, and many teeth.

By children playing with things that can be counted at first to ten and then to a hundred, numbers become familiar and friendly. Children can make a list of the numbers that are important to them such as birthdays, the ages of brothers and sisters . . . The number of the house or flat where a child lives is used as a name: 6, Orchard Lane would be just as identifiable as 'Rose Cottage', Orchard Lane.

It is important for children to develop the concept of size, to have an idea what say 5 marbles and 5 footballs look like.

The concepts of size, volume and quantity have to be developed. 100 marbles may go into a jar, 100 footballs will not. Estimating skills develop. How many marbles, how many tennis balls, how many footballs can be put in a desk or a box? What happens when the box chosen is smaller or bigger? It is important that children learn what numbers are sensible. This is an invaluable skill to develop. As adults we are bombarded with numbers and data that question our credulity.

When the physical idea of cardinal numbers has been grasped then pictures and drawings can be used. But do not move children too quickly to written arithmetic.

Ordinal numbers should follow. The idea that one block can be picked up and given the ordinal number, for example, third is not a natural one. Children will be used to queuing and this is useful experience. They understand being first, second and last in a queue.

Patterns help children to count efficiently - in 2s or 3s or 5s and 10s. Anyone who has worked in a warehouse or checked an order knows how difficult it can be to count accurately. How much easier it is to count and check 100 items grouped in lots of 10. Errors in counting can be hidden as mistakes in adding up. Children need to learn about the conservation of number, that if a group of marbles or blocks is moved on the table the numbers do not change. They have to develop a system that tells them which items have been counted and which have not, learn to touch or group the marbles or blocks. They need to learn to group counters in say 2s, 3s, 4s, 5s . . . This leads later to multiplication and place value.

Keeping tally is a particularly useful technique.

Children also need to know about even and odd numbers, square numbers, triangular numbers and how these can fit together to make squares.

Number lines are useful. These should indicate that they are not finite and that numbers continue after the line has ended. Putting their personal numbers on the line reinforces ideas of ordering, succession and ordinal numbers.

ADDITION

This can be taught as 'counting on' using a number line. Counting out two sets of counters to represent the numbers and then counting them altogether is long and tedious. Keep this method to a minimum. Using a number line is quicker and more efficient. The child begins with the bigger number and counts on the smaller one. This introduces the need to choose which is the bigger.

FIND THE DIFFERENCE

Subtraction is counting back. Cuisenaire rods are useful. Children can either count back from the big number to the small one or count on from the smaller one as shopkeepers do when giving change.

Shopping is a particularly good activity because children have experience of it. A classroom shop is a must and later, picture shopping allows more variety.

MEASURING AND UNITS

Children need practice in measuring and estimating.
Non-uniform non standard units. Let them decide how they can measure things in the classroom using hand-spans, strides, feet, crayons, pencils . . . They soon realise that these units are unsatisfactory. The question why do people get different answers starts a lively discussion often with surprising comments.
Uniform non standard units. Multilink, Cuisenaire Rods, Unifix, playing cards and coins.
Standard Units. Although the basic standard is SI units, children are already used to a mixture of units - a quarter of sweets, a gallon of petrol and a litre of milk . . .

Practical work is essential if children are to gain an understanding of measuring and units that will benefit them all their lives.

Children need to accept the conservation of length, to accept that moving an object does not change its length.

Suppose a desk measures 'seven pencils' across. At first the child needs to see seven pencils laid end to end. Only later will it be acceptable to use one pencil and place it repeatedly seven times across the desk. Children believe what they see. (A kind of wisdom lost when we grow up.) If two pencils are of the same length and one juts out, then they are likely to think that the one jutting out is longer than the other. At all times encourage the children to estimate size.

The stages are

> Direct comparison - he/she is shorter, taller than . . .
> Indirect comparison - with some agreed mark on a chart.
> Indirect comparison using several units laid end to end.
> Indirect comparison with one unit repeated many times.
> Measuring using uniform units.
> Measuring using standard units.
> Computations involving SI units.

Units are needed for length, area, capacity, weight and time.

PLACE VALUE AND NUMBER PAIRS

It is important that children learn number facts and skills in context and that they practise them in a practical way so that the work is relevant to everyday life. They must feel the work is creative, exciting and fun. Use games as much as possible.

Place value follows from an understanding of grouping. Base 10 work requires childen to be able to count to 100 before they can get into the third column - a daunting task for all. To work to base 3, a child needs 9 objects and for base 4 they need 16. These numbers are more easily handled.

When the children are comfortable with exchanging in lower bases then they are ready to work in base 10. Blocks, rods and squares can be used. Children working in pairs will make the task of counting 100 beads easier. Later the abacus is useful.

MULTIPLICATION AND DIVISION

It is debatable whether to teach division before multiplication because children learn about 'sharing' at a very early stage.

Multiplication is repeated addition and children begin with groups or sets. Small groups (say 3 or 4 marbles) are laid out in rows and counted so that the children understand the number in one row, two rows, three rows, and so on. That is two lots, three lots . . .

It is important that they understand that mulitiplication involves numbers of identical sets and develop a sense of pattern.

Mark every 3rd figure in a 0 to 99 number square so that 3 and all multiples of 3 are coloured. This shows the pattern and gives a 'feel' as to how the numbers behave. Make a 0 - 99 number square on 2 cm squared paper and

use with Multilink. Place say a red block on every even number, a green one on every 3rd number and a yellow on every 4th number. This builds up a 3D picture of factors and products. Children soon understand what is happening when more than one colour occurs on a square.

Examine the way in which a rectangle with 12 or 24 squares can be drawn.

Commutativity. It is important that children understand this. The equivalence of 4 x 3 and 3 x 4 can be shown by rearranging four groups of 3 marbles into three groups of 4 marbles. The children will suggest more examples. This is also shown in a 1 - 10 multiplication square.

```
1   2   3   4   5   6   7   8   9   10
2   4   6   8   10  12  14  16  18  20
3   6   9   12  15  18  21  24  27  30
4   8   12  16  20  24  28  32  36  40
5   10  15  20  25  30  35  40  45  50
6   12  18  24  30  36  42  48  54  60
7   14  21  28  35  42  49  56  63  70
8   16  24  32  40  48  56  64  72  80
9   18  27  36  45  54  63  72  81  90
10  20  30  40  50  60  70  80  90  100
```

Children need to make this square on large squared paper. It is symmetrical about its leading diagonal. This shows commutativity clearly, that is 3 x 4 is the same as 4 x 3 in the square and so on. When children are learning tables they need to learn only half of them.

Division is sharing or repeated subtraction. Children need practice in sharing things out equally (dealing cards, dividing piles of marbles and counters) and in moving backwards along a number line. Arrays and squares of counters are helpful.

Consider 24 + 6. Use 6 rows of 4 counters or Multilink, then 4 can be taken away six times. Repeat with several numbers and factors until the children are confident. Once they understand that division is the opposite process to multiplication they will obtain answers from their tables.

Long multiplication and long division are now almost always done with calculators.

RELATIONSHIPS BETWEEN DIFFERENT OPERATIONS

Children should be able to understand the relationship between the four operations and a simple diagram helps.

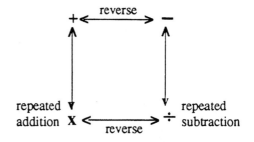

ZERO AND NEGATIVE NUMBERS

Discuss the situations in which zero is used in everyday life. The weather forecast uses zero and there is a zero on a thermometer. Zero is essential as a 'place holder'. Children will also see it easily in the pattern of 10s.

Negative Numbers. These can be difficult to accept and it may be necessary to return to them again at a later stage. Initially, they may be considered as below zero. If zero is taken as the base mark then above this, numbers are positive and below they are zero. Two illustrations help. First, use a thermometer with 0° for freezing on the Celsius scale. Negative temperatures represent those below freezing. Next, consider a lift. If the ground floor is zero, the floor above is floor 1 while the basement is -1. Negative numbers can be shown on a number line. In one way, negative numbers are a mathematical contrivance, a device enabling us to handle such situations as

$$2 - 5 = -3$$

Children have to learn the rules that allow them to handle negative numbers.

SORTING

Being able to sort and classify are very important skills. They form the basis of organisation. Begin with things familiar to the children. They will have no difficulty in sorting a mixed pile of gloves, shoes, hats and scarves or sorting them out in a different way according to their owners. Each group forms a set. Children are familiar with laundry being sorted out at home - whites, coloureds, delicates, hot water wash. Choices are often intuitive but they should be able to explain their selections.

Attribute cards help to develop ways of choosing and organising. These can be drawn to vary in two or more ways. For example 25 to 30 cards can be drawn of a teapot which has or does not have a spout or a handle. This gives rise to several sets. [With handle and spout, without handle and spout, with handle but no spout and with spout but no handle. The teapots can be the same or different.]

Sets and Complements. Most early work concentrates on belonging or not belonging. This leads to dealing with objects that belong to more than one set. For example a collection of red plastic objects in one set and a collection of wooden blocks in another set. What happens to a red wooden block?

Intersection and Union. It can be difficult for children to accept that something can belong to two sets at the same time. Use large hoops on the floor so that there is good visual impact. Details of pets owned by the class lead to a set of dogs, a set of cats, a set of rabbits and so on. These, it is easily understood, all belong to a bigger set of pets. It is often not necessary or desirable to use the words 'intersection' and 'union'.

Venn Diagrams. The hoops lead on to Venn diagrams. Start with familiar situations - breakfast foods, the way in which children travel to school, favourite TV programmes or sports.

TIME

Begin with the activities children know about. The structure of the day - the time they get up, have breakfast, go to school, when school starts and finishes, the time they go home. Go on to ways in which time can be measured. including a water clock, an egg timer, a candle clock, a sundial, shadow clock and pendulum clock. Discuss the clocks the children have at home leading to analogue and digital clocks and watches. Discuss how time 'feels' and why it seems to pass slowly or quickly.

Telling the Time. Begin with the hours and go on to half and quarter hours - quarter to and quarter past, big hands and small hands on clock faces. Explain minutes and seconds. Children find it easy to read digital clocks but are not always sure what they mean. Make a time chart for the day and individual timetables. Estimate how much can be done in three minutes, how long it takes to tidy the room, change for PE, travel home, length of a lesson. Children can close their eyes and raise their hands when they think a minute has passed.

Time on a Longer Scale. Other ways in which the passing of time is measured: days, weeks, months and years. Make a calendar and relate the months to seasons and annual events such as holidays and festivals. The importance of measuring time - schedules and timetables, time zones. Look at photographs and newspapers to illustrate changes with time and the idea of past, present and future. What will children be doing tomorrow, at the weekend, on their holidays? Children confuse size with age - bigger seems to mean older. They understand candles on a birthday cake. Plan a journey. Look at timetables for buses and trains and possible routes for going by car. Make a time line starting 15 years ago to the end of the century.

'WEIGHT'

What is meant by 'weight'. How are things weighed? Use a variety of scales including bathroom scales, kitchen scales, spring balance and classroom balance. Discuss units and the need for different kinds of scales and units. How would you weigh a button, a baby, an adult, an animal? What units would be used? Use marbles as weights before going on to standard weights. This is an area where children can have plenty of practice at estimating. First of all which is heavier or lighter and then estimates of actual weights. Children can also balance themselves on a seesaw and note what happens as they move further from or closer to the fulcrum. (No theory about this, of course.) Use non standard units and then standard units. (Pounds, half pounds, quarters, ounces, kilograms, grams.) How is food sold by weight in shops? Look at labels. Cooking gives excellent practice. Vary recipies according to the number of portions or cakes/biscuits/burgers needed. Weigh bread or cake over a period of a week and note what happens to the weight. Why does this happen?

FRACTIONS

Half and Quarter. Initially, children can work with the idea of a half as one of two pieces not necessarily of the

same size. They need practice in halving a variety of items such as a peeled orange, a piece of plasticine and a handful of beads or marbles. As the concept of equal parts develops, they have to think of ways in which to divide exactly into two - counting, weighing, folding and so on. The division of 50p into two introduces more suggestions. The work is then extended into quarters. Here they need to divide a half again using say an orange, Cuisenaire rods or Colour Factor. Their experience may include cooking - half a cup, half a block of butter, and sharing food in the family or with friends. They will also be familiar with some of the class taking part in different activities such as swimming. When they have a firm idea of what is meant by a half and a quarter it is safe to transfer to drawings on paper. Introduce other fractions as part of a whole. Let children estimate a fraction of of th esize of objects such as the length of a broom handle or the height of a door.

Equivalence of Fractions. Build up families of fractions so that children understand the mathematical link between them and what they mean. Duplicate 4 x 4 squares and divide in half in as many times as possible. Go on to 8 x 8 squares. Use Cuisenaire rods to make a fraction wall with a long rod at the bottom and smaller ones representing fractions above it. Draw fraction graphs. Use equivalent fractions with the numerator on the x axis and the denominator on the y axis. All the members of one set of equivalent fractions will lie on the same graph. Draw graphs for different sets.

RATIOS

A ratio compares two numbers. Unitary ratios have a numerator of 1. Fractions are a form of ratios. To make true comparisons the units for both quantities should be the same. Thus, 1p : £1 is actually 1:100 and 1 cm : 1 km is 1: 100 000.

Scaling. This means making things bigger or smaller but keeping the relative proportions of all the measurements the same. Examine maps and work out distances. Children will be familiar with model cars and planes. Later, they can examine what happens to areas when lengths are changed.

PERCENTAGES

These should be treated as a special kind of fraction in which the denominator is 100. Percentages enable comparisons to be made. Suppose 1 child out of a group of 10 is absent and 2 children out of a group of 25 are away. Compare absenteeism as a percentage. Children need to make as many comparisons as possible using fractions and percentages. They need to understand that a small percentage of a large sum of money may be worth more than a bigger percentage of a small sum and the practical implications of this in real life.

Interest. Begin with simple calculations to show the usefulness of this. A simple brief comment on its applications to banking and mortgages brings this work into the 'real' world.

DECIMALS

These are best introduced through money using either actual or imitation coins. Children should begin by laying out coins for sums uuder £1. Find out how many ways 5p, 10p, 20p and 50p can be laid out. The class shop is the best way of teaching this. Use percentages to reduce prices and introduce bargain offers. Compare offers and decide which is the best.

Decimals and Fractions. Understand that decimals of less than 1 are really fractions with a special denominator of 10, 100 . . . Use a 100 square to show the relationship between 0·1 and 0·2 and 0·5 and so on. Practise changing decimals into fractions and vice versa. How are recurring decimals formed?

Mulitiplying by 10 and 100. Children need to know the associative law of multiplication. For example

$$30 \times 509$$
$$= (3 \times 10) \times 509$$
$$= 3 \times (10 \times 509).$$

Avoid saying 'add a nought'.
Ask the children about the importance of 10 in our decimal currency. For example

10	10 pence pieces make £1
10	5 pence pieces make 50p
5	10 pence pieces make 50p
10	2 pence pieces make 20p
2	10 pence pieces make 20p

and so on.
Examine what happens when decimals are multiplied by 10 or 100.

APPROXIMATE ANSWERS

Children know from their practical work on measuring that there is a limit to how accurate such measurements can be. This means that when the figure contains several digits, some of them may have little meaning in practice. It is necessary to decide what is sensible. Children need to know

to the nearest 10 or 100
to the nearest whole number
to 1 or 2 decimal places
to 1 or 2 significant figures.

These answers are not less accurate, they are not estimates or guesses, they take into account the accuracy required or that is sensible.

POWERS OF WHOLE NUMBERS

Science and technology sometimes use very large numbers and these can be written in index notation or as powers of whole numbers. For example,

$$4 = 2 \times 2 = 2^2$$
$$25 = 5 \times 5 \text{ or } 5^2$$
while $16 = 2 \times 2 \times 2 \times 2 \text{ or } 2^4$

Similarly

$$100 = 10 \times 10 = 10^2$$

and

$$1000 = 10 \times 10 \times 10 = 10^3.$$

Use calculators to explore the rapid growth that occurs when a number is multiplied by itself repeatedly. Even with the number two as in binary fission, the increase is rapid and staggering.

CALCULATORS

As calculators come to be used more freely, it is possible to tackle different kinds of work. Calculators do not necessarily mean that children do not learn their tables or basic arithmetic. Estimated answers ensure that the principles and methods involved are understood. Suppose a child is asked to find two consecutive numbers which when mulitplied together equal 1260. This is tedious by traditional methods. [Estimation suggests the numbers lie between 30 and 40. The calculator gives $34 \times 35 = 1190$ and $35 \times 36 = 1260$.] The calculator offers a good way of testing if place value is understood. The child is asked to remove the digits of a 3 or 4 digit number one at a time by subtraction until zero is left. To eliminate say 853 it is necessary to subtract 3, 50 and 800 (in any order). Clear thinking is encouraged by using calculators as function machines. A constant operation (say 5 x) is fed into the calculator and the children then feed in a series of numbers pressing the = button after each number is fed in. The numbers in and the numbers out are recorded on paper and the process repeated without touching the clear button. From a series of readings, the children work out the value of the constant.

PROBABILITY

Talk about many kinds of events and discuss whether they are likely to happen or not. Always draw on the children's experiences.

John will be ? next birthday.
The new baby will be a boy.
The new baby will be a girl.
There will be lessons on Saturday.
It will snow on Christmas Day.

Let the children place events on a probability line from 0 to 1.

Consider all the possibilities when a die is thrown and when two dice are thrown. From a table of all possibilities find the most common total.

INVESTIGATIONS
AND PROBLEM SOLVING

Investigation. This is fundamental to all subjects but it is particularly important in mathematics. It is vital in the process of developing mathematical thinking.

Children acquire information which has to be sorted and classified. They then hypothesize, test and predict. A high degree of organisation is needed. The question 'What if . . .?' calls for logical and hypothetical proposals. They have to be prepared to revise ideas and evaluate negative evidence. Finally, they have to justify and explain their discoveries and conclusions to others.
Problem Solving. When problems are tackled in groups, children learn social skills as well. They learn to co-operate, to listen to each other, discuss other people's ideas, to try out suggestions and to allow others and themselves to be wrong.

ALGEBRA
LEVELS 2 - 6

NUMBER PATTERNS

Start by reinforcing material dealt with earlier. It is important that the children are confident in all the work using **numbers only** before symbols are introduced.

The detection of pattern and the conclusions that can be drawn form the basis of algebra. Children learn to recognise and use particular attributes of numbers such as odd or even. They know about the numbering of houses and flats; often rows have even numbers on one side and odd numbers on the other. Children learn to use a symbol for a number that is missing. This is the beginning of equations. They need to practise dealing with number patterns, to recognise multiples of 2, 5 and 10 and to be able to deal with sequences and work out what comes next. Use squared paper to lay out square and triangular numbers. Children enjoy building triangular numbers and magic squares.

PRIME NUMBERS

These have already been explored but should be reviewed. Remember 1 is not normally included as a prime number.

FUNCTION MACHINES

Function machines encourage children to find answers to Why? How? and What if? In/Out exercises with a secret constant or operation fed into the machine can only be done by trial and error and by discovering the relationship between the numbers fed into the machine and those coming out. LOGO is particularly useful at this stage.

Look for patterns in addition and multiplication squares, and explore ways of tackling calculations.

FORMULAE AND EQUATIONS

Generalisation is essential to mathematics but children need to be warned not to draw hasty conclusions. Begin with 'think of a number' games. Use function machines as a lead to symbols. Encourage the children to write down what each function machine is doing. Allow them to use whatever words and symbols they choose. Discussion of their answers will lead to suggestions of suitable symbols and the ways in which these formulae can be handled. It is important that the children feel in control at all times.

CO-ORDINATES

Two skills are developed when plotting points. There is the ability to read across and down as when reading a timetable and the understanding that the position of a point can be determined by an ordered pair of numbers. Begin with squared paper and two numbered axes. The points can be envisaged as addresses reached by going along the road and up the steps.

It is essential that the children understand that the point for example (3,2) is different from the point (2,3). They should have plenty of practice in plotting points on the grid and reversing the co-ordinates. Draw simple shapes or their initials in large capitals and write down the co-ordinates necessary to define these shapes. If children work in pairs they can exchange this information and try to draw each other's shapes. This is not as easy as it might seem.

A map of the school and its surroundings extends the work into a practical application and can be followed by a map of where a child lives. Much can be learned from making a detailed street map in which the squares rather than the lines are numbered. The work is difficult involving children pacing the streets and using compasses.

Explore what happens to the co-ordinates when a shape is moved along an axis anywhere on the grid or when the co-ordinates of the shape are mulitplied by 2 or 2 is added to them. They should now be able to decide how to stretch a shape in any direction or enlarge it.

GRAPHS

Table graphs are particularly easy to plot. When the children are confident about the use of co-ordinates then the tradtional x and y axes can be introduced. They can now start to draw lines such as x = 3, y = 4, y = x and so on to simple equations. They should understand that only two points are needed for a straight line (or two and one to check).

Functions. As with the use of function machines, if a set of numbers can be transformed into another set by carrying out some simple function then it is possible to draw a graph of this function by using the linked numbers as co-ordinates. Suppose 2 becomes 5, 3 becomes 6 and 4 becomes 7. Then the points plotted would be (2,5) (3,6) and (4,7). When children are looking for the function, they soon learn to ask what happens to 1 and 0 because the transformations are easy.

Four quadrants. Some graphs can be attempted which use negative quantities.

EQUIVALENT FRACTION GRAPHS

Use two equivalent fractions. Read the numerator as the x co-ordinate and the denominator as the y co-ordinate for each fraction. Draw the graph through the points and the origin and extend to the edge of the graph paper. Other equivalent fractions can be read off the graph. Try with different sets of equivalent fractions.

SIMPLE EQUATIONS

Children should be able to cope withthe graphs of simple linear and polynomial equations such as

$$y = 2x + 3$$
$$3y + 2x = 8$$
$$x^2 = 16$$

MAPPINGS

If children plot different but related mappings they can form a good basis for discussion.

SHAPE AND SPACE
LEVELS 2 - 6

2-D SHAPES

Children should have had experience in sorting shapes of all types and should be able to recognise 2-D shapes. They need to recognise squares, rectangles, circles, triangles, hexagons and pentagons and be able to describe their properties. It is important that they see shapes in all kinds of positions, for example, triangles not always with the base line horizontal.

Squares and Rectangles. They should know in which ways these are similar and in which ways they are different. Squares are special kinds of rectangles. [Other quadrilaterals include kite, rhombus, trapezium and parallelogram.]

Circles. Distinguish between circles and ovals. Know the meaning of half and quarter circles, diameter and radius.

Triangles. Include acute-angled, equilateral, isosceles, right-angled and obtuse triangles.

ANGLES

Children should first see an angle as a measurement of the 'amount of turn or rotation'. An angle should be seen as dynamic not static. There are numerous examples from door handles to cooker knobs, from wheels to water taps. Estimating angles is a worthwhile skill to develop.

Right Angles. These are everywhere: the angle at the elbow can be a right angle as can the angle between the thumb and the hand. Look for right angles in the classroom, then identify them in squares, rectangles and right-angled triangles.

Compass. Relate angles to the points of the compass. Find north. In which direction is the school hall, the playground? Look at maps and discuss the ways in which a compass helps travellers. Discuss how to use a map of your town or area. Look at an ordnance survey map. Use orienteering.

Bearings. This uses work done on co-ordinates and scale. Choose a base line such as the school fence or a line marked on the ground. Children measure the angle an object makes with the base line at a chosen point. The distance from this point to the base of the object is measured. When these measurements are put on a right angled triangle drawn to scale, they can work out the height of the object. Next, two sets of measurements are made from two different places on the base line. These can be used to draw a triangle to scale. From this children can work out their distances from the object and the height of the object above the base line. Discuss the use of bearings to explorers and in navigation. Once ships had to take bearings at two different times having travelled to the second place on the sea (their base line). Now there are charts for the second reading. Introduce latitude, longitude, time zones and international date lines. There may be navigational charts in the local museum while a visit to the 'bridge' on a ship gives an entirely new perspective to this work.

3-D SHAPES

The world is a 3-D place. Look at 3-D shapes in the classroom and discuss common factors. Then study a selection of 3-D mathematical shapes.

Cube. Six faces, each face being a square. Look for the right-angles. Three faces meet at each corner or vertex.

Octahedron. Eight faces, each being an equilateral triangle. Four faces meet at each vertex.

Cubes and Cuboids. Discuss where these can be found. Cubes - ice cube, sugar, stock, die. Cuboids - suitcase, computer, shoe box, pencil box. Count faces and corners. Cut open a box and discuss the changes this makes.

Cylinders. Let children collect examples. Cut open the cardboard roll of a toilet roll and examine the change this makes to the shape. Let children make a cylinder. Cylinders - vacuum cleaner, hose pipe, pencil, washing-up liquid container.

Spheres. Collect spheres of different sizes - marbles, beads, tennis balls.

MOVEMENT

In PE have children move in one direction (translational) and then turn (rotational). In Art, children can paint with blocks and move the blocks sideways or turn them. They should understand turning clockwise or anticlockwise.

UNITS OF MEASUREMENT

Length. It is important to understand what happens when a piece of string or rope is coiled. Its length remains the same as when it is uncoiled. Revise units used to measure length, for example, for height, distance, the length and breadth of the classroom.

Capacity. This is how much a container will hold. Consider the capacities of bottles, cartons, jars, jugs and cans. Revise units and choose containers that will allow conclusions to be made, for example, a litre, 500 ml, 250 ml and so on. How many times can a small bottle be filled from a big one? Distinguish between volume and capacity. Volume involves the external measurements of the container.

'Weight' (Mass). Discuss kinds of scales and what each is used for. Consider the weights of packets of cereal, biscuits and sugar. [In secondary school, children will be able to distinguish between weight and mass.]

SYMMETRY

The idea of symmetry is based on the premise that things can be moved around and still look the same. Children often have an instinctive understanding of symmetry and

will make their drawings and models as symmetrical as they can. Children can make drawings with matching halves and 'butterfly' ink blots in the fold of a piece of paper. Use safe plastic mirrors and drawings and pictures to make examples of symmetry. Make half drawings that will be complete when viewed in the mirror. Place a mirror on letters and drawings and examine the reflections. Discuss the symmetry of letters, numbers and 2-D shapes. Look for a plane of symmetry in a 3-D shape.

CONGRUENCY

Shapes are congruent when they are identical (except for location). If two squares are cut out and placed on top of each other, they are congruent if they cover each other exactly. This condition must be true for any two shapes to be congruent. Squares, cubes, equilateral triangles and circles are always similar but they are not always congruent. Rectangles, isosceles triangles, cuboids and ellipses are not necessarily similar. Make shapes and drawings and give children practice in deciding which are congruent and which are similar.

ROTATIONAL SYMMETRY

Begin with a coloured square. Ask children to close their eyes and turn the square through a quarter turn. When they open their eyes, they cannot tell the square has been turned. It has a rotational symmetry of 4. If it had been turned through a one-eighth turn it would have looked different. Therefore, a square does not have a rotational symmetry of 8. Place a thin piece of paper against the carbon side of a piece of carbon paper. Fold in half with the thin paper outside. Fold in half again and then along the diagonal. Draw a simple pattern on the outside, pressing hard. When the paper is opened and the carbon paper removed, the paper will have a pattern with a rotational symmetry of 8.

Rotational symmetry is used in wallpaper and in the design of tiles. Look for it in school and at home.

PERIMETERS

Measure the perimeters of the classroom, hall and playground. Record the measurements as length and breadth. Draw squares and rectangles on squared paper and count the squares which make up the edges. Lead the children to discover the relationship between length, breadth and perimeter. Draw irregular shapes on squared paper and get children to estimate the perimeters in terms of squares.

AREAS

Discuss the meaning of area. Look at the drawings on squared paper used to find perimeters. Count the squares to obtain the areas. Let children work out the relationship between length and breadth for squares and rectangles. Next, draw a diagonal across each of the squares and rectangles. Each clearly contains two triangles. Children should now be able to work out the area of a triangle. It

is important that they understand that it is the vertical or perpendicular height of the triangle that matters.

VOLUMES

Begin by filling **cubes and cuboids** with small cubes. The children can see that the volume of the bigger cube is equal to the volume of all the little cubes. If we imagine that they are unit cubes the volume is equal to the number of cubes. This leads to explaining and showing that the number of cubes along the length multiplied by the number along the width multiplied by the number high gives the same total as physically filling the big cube. The little cubes can be removed from the large cube and stacked outside and counted one by one. They can repeat with several cubes and cuboids finally ending with

Volume = Length x Width (Breadth) x Height (Depth)

Triangular Prism. This can be imagined as a stack of triangles. Its volume is therefore the area of the triangular face of the prism multiplied by its height.

CIRCLES

Begin by cutting out several circles of different sizes. The children then measure the circumferences. There are two convenient ways to do this. They can place a piece of string around the circumference and then measure it with a ruler or they make a mark on the circumference and roll the circle along a line beginning and ending with the mark touching the line. The distance the mark has moved equals the circumference. In each case also measure the diameter. The results of all the class measurements are tabulated. It should be apparent that the circumference is a little more than three times the diameter. This can also be shown by plotting a graph of diameter/circumference. The children have now encountered pi. A calculator will show that pi is not an easy number. Over a million calculations have been made to obtain a precise result. The usual value is 3·142 which is close to 22/7.

$$\frac{\text{Circumference}}{\text{Diameter}} = \pi$$

$$= 3\cdot142 \text{ to 3 dec. pl.}$$

$$\text{or} \quad = \frac{22}{7}$$

Area of a Circle. Draw a circle on squared paper and count the little squares in it. This does not give very accurate results. An improvement is to count the little squares in a big square into which a circle just fits and the little squares in a square which just fits inside the circle. The area of the circle must be somewhere between the two areas. Lead the children to discover that the circle can be divided into triangular segments. Fold a circle in half,

then in half again and again and again. Open it out and mark alternate segments. Cut out the segments and lay 'head to toe' to form a rectangle. The length of this is half the circumference and the width is the radius of the circle.

The area of the rectangle is length x width.

$$\text{Area} = \frac{1}{2} \text{circumference x radius}$$

$$= \frac{1}{2} \times \pi \times \text{diameter x radius}$$

$$= \frac{1}{2} \times \pi \times 2 \text{ radius x radius}$$

$$= \pi \text{ Radius}^2$$

$$= \pi r^2 \text{ where r is the radius.}$$

3-D SHAPES

Use dotty paper to draw some 3-D shapes. Look at the ways in which artists use perspective.

ENLARGING

Maps and models show the effects of scaling. Draw rectangles on a graph so that a line through the origin passes through the top right corner of each of the rectangles. Look at the relationships between the dimensions of these rectangles. Work out what happens to areas when the lengths and breadths are doubled or halved. Use the photocopier to produce different magnifications.

TESSELLATION

Children will be familiar with tiles on walls and floors. Odd 'end of stock' tiles from DIY stores are useful as examples of patterns. They may have rough edges but paper outlines are safe for the children and make an interesting beginning. To tessellate regularly, the 2-D shapes must form 360° at their junction. Using reflection, rotation and transformation, children can produce a variety of patterns which when coloured make excellent displays.

HANDLING DATA
LEVELS 2 - 6

SORTING AND CLASSIFYING

Nowadays, we are surrounded by an ever increasing avalanche of information and technical data. It pours from computers and media in a never ending stream. Even government ministers are unable to cope with all the data that crosses their desks. Learning to extract information that is relevant and useful to us is a valuable skill. It is important that children learn to analyse data, ask questions about what is being presented and why, and if it is really necessary. A study of advertising gives endless examples of the ways in which information is analysed and presented. Ask the children to decide what is being emphasized and what exactly is being said about the product.Their comments usually show remarkable discernment.

Begin with the familiar such as a pile of mixed clothing. Children need to understand that with a universal set of data there may be subsets defined by different characteristics or attributes. It is necessary to decide how the data is to be sorted. This depends on the kind of data and the nature of the investigation, that is the kind of conclusions to be drawn. For example, consider a pile of mixed clothing - scarves, gloves, mittens, socks, shoes, hats . . Is the investigation about the number of scarves, the number of gloves (in pairs or singles?), or is it about who wears what, or is it about colour or the material used to make the clothes? The information to be collected will decide how the items are to be sorted, what sets are to be created: a set of scarves, a set of gloves . . . or a set of John's clothing, a set of Mary's clothing . . .

Mostly, the data cannot be physically sorted in this way but is recorded as information on paper. The way in which it is to be recorded is very important. Classification and the way in which the information is to be processed are linked.

Information. Decide on what information is needed.

Information Record Sheet. Plan how the information is to be recorded. Allow for the unexpected.

Observations. Decide how the information is to be obtained - by observation or questionnaire . . . If we do not make the relevant observations or ask the appropriate questions then we shall not collect the data we need. Discuss whether the way in which the questions are worded will affect the replies.

Conclusions. Decide the nature of the results.

Using the results. The conclusions may not be what is expected. Discuss the ways in which the results can be presented and the effects of these different presentations.

LISTS AND TABLES

These are probably the simplest way of handling data. They may be organised in several ways such as alphabetically, by size, by geographical location, in order of importance and so on.

Tally and Frequency Tables. These are particularly useful when counting is involved as in, for example, an analysis of traffic. The children simply make a mark on their recording sheet each time they count one of the vehicles. One child or a pair counts one kind of vehicle only and the class results are put together.

GRAPHS AND DATA

Block Graphs. In these each column is discrete and the blocks are clearly marked. Each column has it own label.

Bar Graphs. The blocks used in block graphs are replaced by continuous bars.

Conversion Graphs. These show the relationship between two units such as temperature on Fahrenheit and Centigrade scales.

Pie Charts. These show the relative proportions of each part of the data collected.

Scatter Graphs. These show two pieces of information about objects in a set at the same time. They are useful when the correlation between the two is not exact: for example, shoe sizes and age. Not all children of the same age take the same size in shoes.

Relationship or Function Graphs. These show the relationship between one variable and another as in a tables graph.

Pictograms. In these the data is represented by symbols or motifs, each symbol represents one or several items.

VENN DIAGRAMS

These are useful for displaying the relationships between sets of objects. They are easy to understand and present a simple way of dealing with items with attributes that place them in two or more sets.

AVERAGES

Mean. If there are n numbers in a set, the mean is the total of the numbers divided by n.

Median. When a series of numbers is arranged in order of size, the middle number is the median. If there is an even number of numbers in the series, the median is the average of the two middle values.

Mode. This is the most popular or most frequently occurring item. If two numbers are equally the most popular then there are two modes.

TREE DIAGRAMS

These show the ways in which items or sets can be subdivided. For example traffic can be divided into commercial and private. Commercial vehicles can be divided into lorries and vans. Private can be divided into cars and bikes. The number of subsets depends on what information is available and needed. Probabilities are also shown on a tree diagram.

GRAPH PAPER (2mm/10mm/20mm)

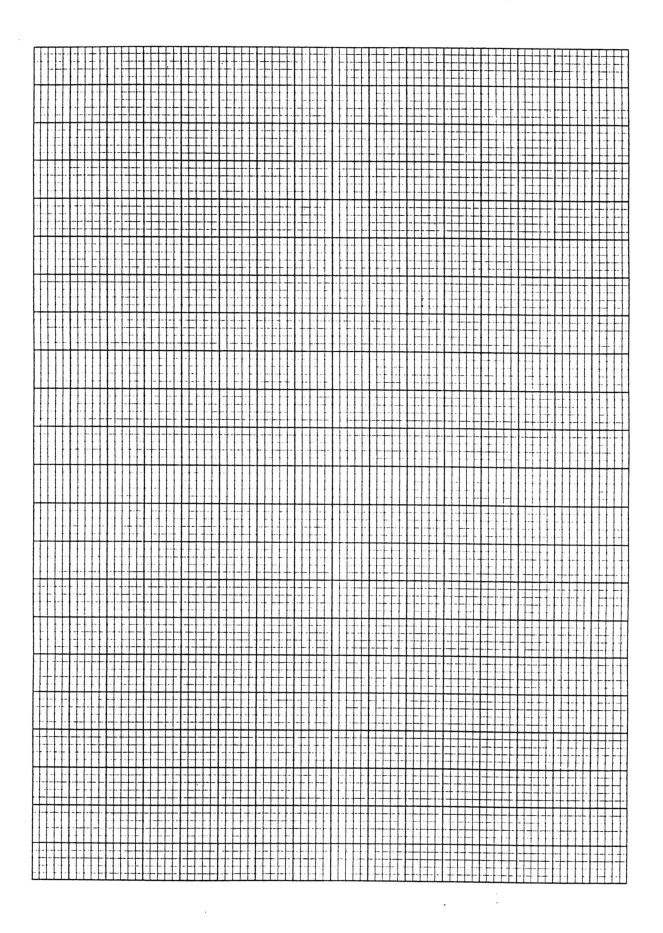

HALF-CENTIMETRE SQUARED PAPER

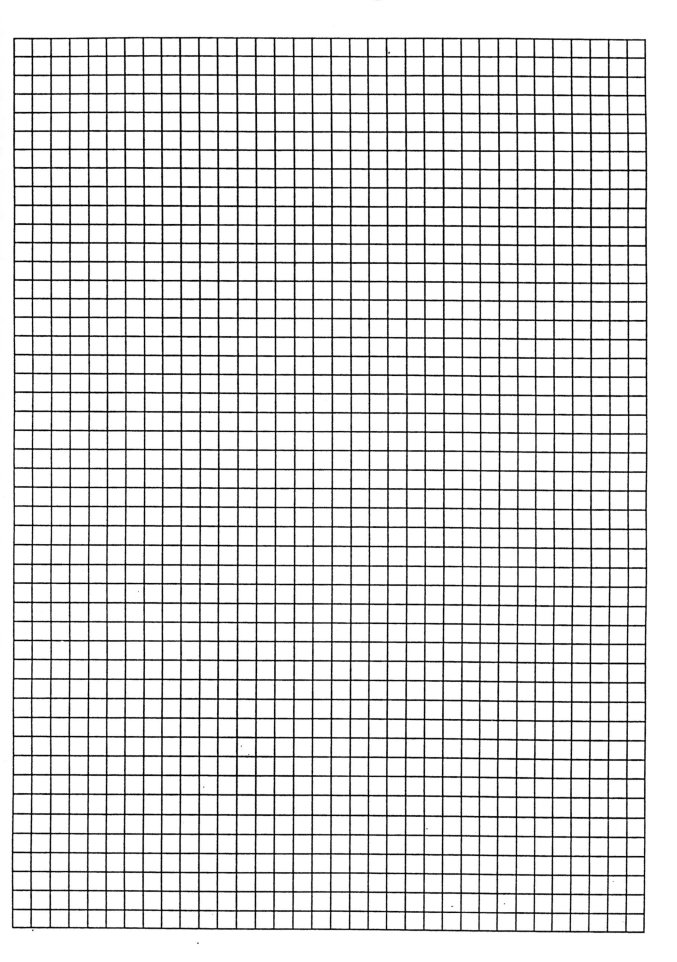

CENTIMETRE SQUARED PAPER

DOTTY PAPER (SQUARES)

DOTTY PAPER (TRIANGLES)

ISOMETRIC PAPER

RECORD SHEET
MATHEMATICS

Name _____ Age _____

Page	Master Copy		Page	Master Copy	
	NUMBER		45	Ratio (L5)	
3	Addition to 10 (L2)		46	Square Roots and Indices (L5)	
4	Addition to 10 (L2)		47	Probability (L5)	
5	Subtraction to 10 (L2)		48	Units (L5)	
6	Subtraction to 10/Fewer (L2)		49	Decimals and Fractions (L6)	
7	Addition and Subtraction Problems (L2)		50	Probability (L6)	
8	Tens and Units (L2)				
9	Dice/Money (L2)			**ALGEBRA**	
10	Ordering and Place Value (L2)		51	Missing Numbers and Symbols (L2)	
11	Shopping and Change (L2)		52	Number Patterns (L2)	
12	Half and Quarter (L2)		53	Function Machines (L3)	
13	Fractions (L2)		54	Addition and Multiplication Squares (L4)	
14	Measuring (L2)		55	Co-Ordinates (L4)	
15	Place Value and Ordering to 1000 (L3)		56	Prime Numbers and Multiples (L5)	
16	Addition and Subtraction to 20 (L3)		57	Equivalent Fractions (L5)	
17	Addition and Subtraction Problems (L3)		58	Flowcharts and Function Problems (L5)	
18	Place Value Cards (L3)		59	Problems (L5)	
19	Place Value Boards (L3)		60	Co-Ordinates (L5)	
20	Pair Bonds to 20 (L3)		61	Graphs (L5)	
20	Number Patterns (L3)		62	Equations (L6)	
21	Bingo (L3)				
22	Five and Ten Times Tables (L3)			**SHAPE AND SPACE**	
23	Multiplication Question Cards (L3)		63	Shapes (L2)	
24	Multipicatione Answer Cards (L3)		64	Quadrilaterals (L2)	
25	Multiplication (L3)		65	Rectangles and Squares (L2)	
26	Division - Question Cards (L3)		66	Right Angles (L2)	
27	Division - Answer Cards (L3)		67	Sorting (L3)	
28	Problems (L3)		68	Similarity and Congruency (L4)	
29	Estimates/Units (L3)		69	Town Map (L4)	
30	Car Boot Sale (L3)		70	Symmetry (L4)	
31	Price Tags (L3)		71	Symmetry (L4)	
32	Time (L3)		72	Areas and Perimeters (L4)	
33	Number Lines/Negative Numbers (L3)		73	Areas (L5)	
34	Function Machines (L4)		74	Circles and Cubes (L6)	
35	Numbers to Base Ten and Two (L4)		75	Tessellations and Networks (L6)	
36	Addition and Subtraction TUs (L4)				
37	Addition and Subtraction HTUs (L4)			**HANDLING DATA**	
38	Mental Arithmetic Cards (L4)		76	Tally and Frequency Charts (L2)	
39	Approximate Answers (L4)		77	Lists and Tables (L3)	
40	Fractions (L4)		78	Bar Charts (L3)	
41	Percentages (L4)		79	Information and Analysis (L4)	
42	Problems (L4)		80	Information and Analysis (L4)	
43	Multiplication and Division (L5)		81	Graphs and Pie Charts (L5)	
44	Approximation (L5]		82	Scatter Graphs (L6)	

ANSWERS

Page 3

Number	Word		
5	five	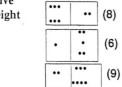	(5)
8	eight		(8)
			(6)
2			
5			(9)
6			

3, 5, 6, 8, 9

Page 4

8	4 and 6
7	5
	6
	10
three 3	9
six 6	8
eight 8	8
seven 7	6
nine 9	10
eight 8	5
ten 10	5
six 6	9
eight 8	9

carriage A 3
carriage B 2
total 6

Page 5

1. 2
2. 4
3. 2
   2
   3
   4
   5
   3
   4

Page 6

1. 3
2. 3   2
   2   2
   3   1
   8   4
   2   2
3. A
   C
   1
   2
   2
   1
   B, C

Page 7

1. 4 dogs
   6 cats
   2
   2 rabbits
   12 animals

Jane's Chart

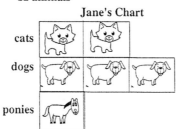

cats
dogs
ponies

2. 5
3. 5
4. 2
5. 2
6. 7
7. 3
8. 3

Page 8

1. 5 tens 6 units   56
   8 tens 5 units   85
   7 tens 1 unit   71
2. 2 units (42) 8 units (28)
3. 6 tens (61)   2 tens (29)
   7 tens (75)
4. 2 tens, 7 units (27)
   9 tens, 6 units (96)

Page 9

Dice: 5
      9
      7

Coins:
8p = 5p, 2p, 1p   14p = 10p, 2p, 2p
9p = 5p, 2p, 2p   16p = 10p, 5p, 1p
13p = 10p, 2p, 1p   17p = 10p, 5p, 2p

Page 10

1. 3, 7, 11, 24, 29, 31, 42, 50, 65, 92
2. 6
   3
   8
   9
   9
   6
   5
3. 5
   92
   40
   5
   24
   11 or 33

Page 11

5p
8p
7p
12p
15p
19p
6p, 5p and 1p
9p, 5p, 2p and 2p
2p, 1p, and 1p
9p, 5p, 2p and 2p
1 can Fizo and 1 bar chocolate
3 cakes or a can of Fizo and chocolate

Page 12

1.

2.

3. $\frac{1}{2}$ $\frac{1}{4}$ $\frac{1}{2}$

   $\frac{1}{2}$ $\frac{1}{4}$

Page 13

1. 3 apples inside
   3 apples outside

2. 4 triangles inside
   4 triangles outside

3. C
   B
   B

4.

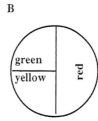

Page 14

4.   A   (i) 4 cm
    C   (ii) 1 cm
    B
    C and F; A and D

5.   5 km   4 km
    8 km   Bearsville
    10 km   and
               Snaptown
               6 km

Page 15
24
39
131
300
102
21
39
43
99
270
36
100

3, 11, 24, 79, 98, 198, 400, 561, 601, 970

24
98 and 198
601
3
970

Page 16
19	13
13	3
16	11
·18	5
18	11
13	15
17	18
6	1
11	12
9	4

5
7   17   19
6   ___ ___
8
3   19   14
3   ___ ___
7
5
4   7   12
0   ___ ___
2

Page 17
1. 7
2. 6
3. 1
4. 8
5. 3
6. 10
7. 14
8. 8
9. 9,   1
10. 9
11. 11
12. 4
13. 37
14. 14
15.   (i) 12
      (ii) 6
      (iii) 18
16.   John, 1

Page 19

tens	units
5	4

hundreds	tens	units
2	0	6

hundreds	tens	units
9	8	2

units
5

tens	units
3	3

hundreds	tens	units
7	4	1

hundreds	tens	units
8	1	7

units
9

hundreds	tens	units
1	3	0

tens	units
5	5

tens	units
1	8

units
1

units
8

units
7

tens	units
7	3

hundreds	tens	units
3	0	0

Page 20
All 20

20	14
19	13
18	12
17	11
16	10
15	Numbers repeat

6	8
10	12
14	16
18	20

8, 10, 12, 14, 16, 18, 20

Page 22
		20
20	25	30
25	35	40
35	45	50
45	55	60

15, 20, 25, 30, 35, 40, 45, 50, 55, 60

	40
30	50
50	60
80	70
100	80
120	90
	100
	110
	120

30, 40, 50, 60, 70, 80, 90, 100, 110, 120

Page 23

2	4	6	8	10
12	14	16	18	20
22	24	5	10	15
20	25	30	35	40
45	50	55	60	10
20	30	40	50	60
70	80	90	100	110
120	9	12	16	6

Page 25

2 x 2

2 x 6   6 x 2   3 x 4   4 x 3

3 x 5   5 x 3

2 x 8   8 x 2   4 x 4

2 x 15   15 x 2   3 x 10   10 x 3
5 x 6   6 x 5

5 x 7   7 x 5

2 x 20   20 x 2   4 x 10   10 x 4
5 x 8   8 x 5

2 x 30   30 x 2   3 x 20   20 x 3
4 x 15   15 x 4   5 x 12   12 x 5
6 x 10   10 x 6

Page 26

1	2	3	4	5
6	7	8	9	10
11	12	1	2	3
4	5	6	7	8
9	10	11	12	1
2	3	4	5	6
7	8	9	10	11
12	3	4	4	5

Page 28
1. £16
2. 4
3. 45p
4. £15
5. 7 £56
6. 6 cans £18
7. 4 bags £3·60
8. 5 gallons
9. 3 boxes
10. 200

Page 29
14. litres   litres
    £ and p   hours
    hands
    mph or km/h
    mph or km/h
    feet or metres
    months or weeks
    years
15. kg   g
    l
    l   l

Page 32
6.

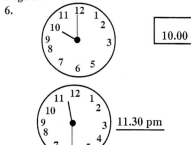

10.00

11.30 pm

7. (i) 7.00   7.55
   (ii) 23.30   1.00

Page 33
1.

0 50 100 150 200 250 300 350
75 125   199   210   330

2. -2 -5 -6

3. 11am ⌐ 5°   10
         ⊢ 0°
    1am ⌐ -5°

4.   -1   0   1   2   3

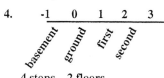

4 stops   2 floors

Page 34

	73
9	
	113

	5
40	
	8

÷ 2   ÷ 2   ÷ 2

18   60

Page 35

302   420   3045

128	62	32	16	8	4	2	1
				1	0	0	1
				1	1	1	1
		1	0	0	1	0	0
	1	1	1	1	0	0	1

3 is 11   9 is 1001   15 is 1111
36 is 100100   121 is 1111001
    Number to base ten
    5
    15
    22

Page 36

37	72	89	94
87	82	45	71
41	14	24	61
49	19	9	34

```
 24      70       27 _     34 _     50 _
 36 +     7 +     12       15       21
  8      42       15       19       29
 10       9
 78     128       64 _     87 _
                   8       30
                  56       57
```

Page 37

799	634	728	730
281	292	96	640

```
 235       5       315 _     120 _
157 +    306 +    204        39
830       92      111        81
1222     403
```

4315
12788

30 000   1 000   900   20 6
70 000   8 000   50   4

Page 38

120	79	72	5
29	11	14	432
97	6 000	14	60
49	24	23	3 000
19	33	4	19
120	49	36	330

Page 39
100 + 500 ——> 600

100 + 200 ——> 300

250 = 266
100 = 105
200 = 172

Page 40

$\frac{1}{4}$ $\frac{1}{3}$ $\frac{1}{2}$

3 circles coloured

$\frac{2}{3}$ = $\frac{6}{9}$ = $\frac{8}{12}$ = $\frac{4}{6}$

$\frac{2}{6}$ = $\frac{1}{3}$ = $\frac{5}{15}$

$\frac{4}{20}$ = $\frac{1}{5}$ = $\frac{8}{40}$ = $\frac{12}{60}$

$\frac{5}{20}$ = $\frac{1}{4}$ = $\frac{2}{8}$ = $\frac{3}{12}$

$\frac{5}{10}$ = $\frac{2}{4}$ = $\frac{1}{2}$

$\frac{1}{8}$ $\frac{1}{6}$ $\frac{1}{5}$ $\frac{1}{4}$ $\frac{1}{3}$

Page 41
1. 45%   60%   80%   75%   80%

2. $\frac{30}{100}$ or $\frac{3}{10}$ $\frac{25}{100}$ or $\frac{1}{4}$

   $\frac{60}{100}$ or $\frac{6}{10}$ or $\frac{3}{5}$

   $\frac{75}{100}$ or $\frac{3}{4}$

   $\frac{90}{100}$ or $\frac{9}{10}$

3. 50%   25%   75%

4. £1   40p   £12   85p

5. £2   £3·15   £6   £9·60

6. 270 boys

7. 50%   30%   20%

8. £22·50

Page 42
1. (i) 0•1mm
   (ii) 32mm
2. 7•2cm
3. 7
4. £1•45
5. 22
6. £18•90
7. 70•30cm
8. 107sec
9. 19hr
   15 hr
10. 18•35*l*

Page 43

11 136	5 974	32 093
35	19	15

estimate 20

4 000	2 800	42 000
10	25	14

estimate £26

£
3•70
0•78
0•68
3•50
1•30
‾‾‾‾
9•96

Page 44
1. 20   150   390   210
2. 300   600   5 800   3 100
3. 60   50   300   300
4. 3•3   7•1   20•1   34•2
5. 45•33   9•11   3•05   2•90
6. 90
7. 43cm
8. 16p
9. £30•30

Page 45
2. Length is 8 000cm or 80 m
   XY = 4cm
   really 40m
   $\frac{1}{2}$
   50%
3. 4cm or 40 mm
4. 200g c apples
   100g butter
   200g flour
   100g c sugar
   $1\frac{1}{2}$ teaspoon bp
5. 6 *l*
6. 108 miles

Page 46
1. 3   4   6   7   8
2. 25   81   100   121   225
3. 64   27   216   8   125
   32   10 000   16   81   1 000 000
4. A = 9cm²   B = 16 cm²
5. X = 36cm²
   $\frac{36\text{cm}^2}{9\text{cm}^2}$ = 4

Page 47
1.

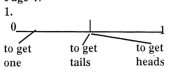
to get   to get   to get
one   tails   heads

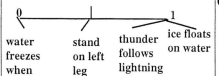
water   stand   thunder   ice floats
freezes   on left   follows   on water
when   leg   lightning
heated

3. $\frac{1}{2}$

$\frac{1}{4}$

$\frac{1}{52}$

4. $\frac{3}{8}$

$\frac{5}{8}$

Page 48
1. g
   mm
   years
   cm
   minutes
   l
   ml
   g
   m

2. 130cm   1500m   3250ml
3. 200
4. 2km
5. 15kg
6. 20g
7. 10
8. 650g

Page 49
1. 0•356
   0•6984
   1•827
2. 0•007
3. 0•3   0•5   0•75   0•25
   0•4   0•15   0•5   0•07

4. $\frac{8}{10} = \frac{4}{5}$ $\frac{5}{100} = \frac{1}{20}$

   $\frac{2}{1\,000} = \frac{1}{500}$ $\frac{5}{10\,000} = \frac{1}{2\,000}$

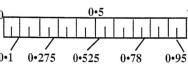
0•1   0•275   0•525   0•78   0•95

6. 30%   50%   75%   25%   15%
7. £55   £63
   £1•75   £100

Page 50
1.

	1	2	3	4	5	6
1	2	3	4	5	6	7
2	3	4	5	6	7	8
3	4	5	6	7	8	9
4	5	6	7	8	9	10
5	6	7	8	9	10	11
6	7	8	9	10	11	12

7

$\frac{1}{36}$

2. $\frac{1}{10}$

3. E = $\frac{1}{11}$ M = $\frac{2}{11}$

   B = 0

4. $\frac{1}{5}$ $\frac{4}{5}$

5. $\frac{1}{8}$ $\frac{1}{4}$

Page 51
1.   9   8   7   6
   5   4   3   2   1

2. even: 14, 12, 8, 22, 4, 18,
        6, 10, 2, 36
   odd: 3, 23, 7, 31, 19, 33,
        1, 25, 5, 21

3. 6+ 1,   5+2,   4+3,   5+1+1
   3+3+1,   2+2+2+1

4.   3   6   3   4
   11   9   6   2   3

Page 52
1. 13, 16, 19
    50, 60, 70
    32, 64, 128
    25, 23, 21
    20, 25, 30
    12, 8, 4
    $\frac{1}{6}$ $\frac{1}{7}$ $\frac{1}{8}$

2. 6, 10, 12, 16, 20, 22, 26, 30
    5, 10, 15, 20, 25, 30
    10, 20, 30

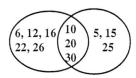

3. $(+1 \div 2)$ $(\times 2 \div 3)$ $(\times 5\ -4)$
    4 ← 6   8 ← 12   15 ← 7

Page 53
1. 12   17   22
2. 14 and 22
3. 6
    20

4.
	5
	17
	29
6	
10	

5. The machine multiplies the
   numbers by 3 and and then adds 2.

Page 54

+	1	2	3	4
1	2	3	4	5
2	3	4	5	6
3	4	5	6	7
4	5	6	7	8

+	2	4	6	8
2	4	6	8	10
4	6	8	10	12
6	8	10	12	14
8	10	12	14	16

+	2	5	10	15
2	4	7	12	17
5	7	10	15	20
10	12	15	20	25
15	17	20	25	30

+	10	20	30	40
10	20	30	40	50
20	30	40	50	60
30	40	50	60	70
40	50	60	70	80

X	1	2	3	4
1	1	2	3	4
2	2	4	6	8
3	3	6	9	12
4	4	8	12	16

X	2	4	6	8
2	4	8	12	16
4	8	16	24	32
6	12	24	36	48
8	16	32	48	64

X	5	10	15	20
5	25	50	75	100
10	50	100	150	200
15	75	150	225	300
20	100	200	300	400

X	3	5	7	9
3	9	15	21	27
5	15	25	35	45
7	21	35	49	63
9	27	45	63	81

Page 55
A (0, 6)
B (2,0)
C (4, 3)
D (7, 5)
E (9,9)

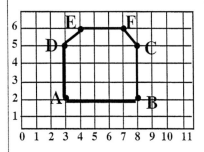

Page 56
1.
1
Multiples of 2
     4, 6, 8, 10,
12, 14, 16, 18, 20,
22, 24, 26, 28, 30,
32, 34, 36, 38, 40,
42, 44, 46, 48, 50,
52, 54, 56, 58, 60
62, 64, 66, 68, 70
72, 74, 76, 78, 80
82, 84, 86, 88, 90
92, 94, 96, 98, 100

Multiples of 3
6, 9, 12, 15, 18
21, 24, 27, 30
33, 36, 39
42, 45, 48
51, 54, 57, 60
63, 66, 69
72, 75, 78
81, 84, 87, 90
93, 96, 99

Multiples of 5	Multiples of 7
10	14
15, 20	21, 28
25, 30	35
35, 40	42, 49
45, 50	56
55, 60	63
65, 70	70, 77
75, 80	84
85, 90	91
95, 100	98

2, 3, 5, 7, 11, 13, 17. 19, 23, 29,
31, 37, 41, 43, 47, 53, 59, 61, 67,
71, 73, 79, 83, 89, 97
Prime

2. 4   9   16   25
    8   27   64   125
    16   81   81   121
    2   4   5   6
    9   10   100   2
    3   4   5   2

Page 57
1.   9   12

2. $\frac{}{4}$ $\frac{}{6}$ $\frac{4}{}$ $\frac{5}{}$ $\frac{6}{}$

     $\frac{3}{8}$ $\frac{}{16}$ $\frac{5}{}$ $\frac{}{24}$

     $\frac{}{10}$ $\frac{}{15}$ $\frac{8}{25}$ $\frac{12}{}$

Page 58
1.

£180
45 hr

1. 9   3. 2
    22   4•5
                   16

2. 18   4. 9
    36   17
    63   21

Page 59
1. nc pence
2. ms g
3. 80 - R
4. (100 - 3N)cm
5. 550ml
6. 4
7. 40 + 150 = £1•90
8.

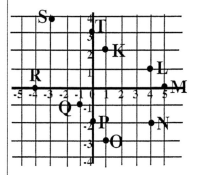

£1•75
£3•00
20 miles
(25m + 50)p where m is the
distance

Page 60
B (2, 3) C (0, 1) D (-2, 2) E (-4, 3)
F (-5, -2) G(-3, -4) H (0, -3) I (2, -4)
J (3, 0)

3. Number of children in class = 24
Alan D3
Helen E2
A1 and F1

Page 61
1.

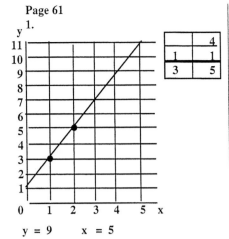

		4
1		1
3		5

y = 9   x = 5

2.

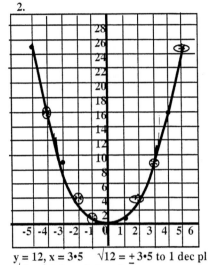

y = 12, x = 3•5   √12 = ± 3•5 to 1 dec pl
√8 = ± 2•8 to 1 dec pl
√14 = ±3•7 to 1 dec pl
√20 = ± 4•5 to 1 dec pl

Page 62
1. x = 4   m = 3
    p = 2   t = 3
    z = 5   s = 4
    y = 5   h = 2
2. 13cm 8cm
3. 17 toffees
4. 5
5. 3 boy + 2 sister = 10 girl ate 4

Page 63
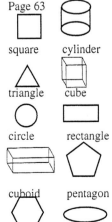

square   cylinder

triangle   cube

circle   rectangle

cuboid   pentagon

hexagon   oval

Page 64
1. A, B
2. A, B, C, D, E

Page 65
1. A, B, C, E
2.

Rect.	Square	Quad. but not a rect or square	Not a quad
B, C	A, H	G, D	F, E

Page 66
1. A, C, G, H
2. B, D, F
3. E, J
4. I, J
5.

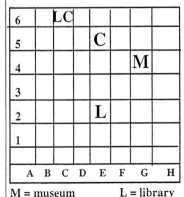

Page 67
B, no right angle   C
B no right angle   has 3 sides

Page 68
B C similar to A
B C congruent to A

A, B, E, D, F similar to A
A, B, D congruent to A

X will have sides of 6 and 4
squares.
Y will have sides in the ratio 6:4

Page 69
shopping centre: C4, D4
railway: A6
bank: north
marina: north east

6	LC						
5			C				
4					M		
3							
2				L			
1							
	A	B	C	D	E	F	G	H

M = museum   L = library
LC = leisure centre   C = castle

Walk east along High Street then
south down Castle Street

Page 70
1.
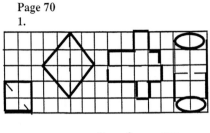

— — — — — lines of symmetry

2.
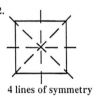

4 lines of symmetry   1 line of symmetry

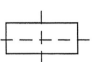

2 lines of symmetry   3 lines of symmetry

nil lines of symmetry   4 lines of symmetry

Page 71
1. A , B, D
2. X, H, S

Page 72
1. A 112 squares   B 28 squares
    112
    28
Area of B is a quarter area of A or
A is 4 times the size of B.
2. 16cm   18cm
3. 14cm
4. 4cm

Page 73

Rectangles length	breadth	area
		240cm²
4cm		
		406 cm²
		36in²
	27ft	

Squares length	breadth	area
25cm	25cm	
30cm	30cm	
4•5ft	4•5ft	
6•3in	6•3in	

Triangles base	perpendicular height	area
		90cm²
15cm		
	30mm	
		6•5in²
	25ft	

Page 74

1. 154cm²   616cm²
    When radius is doubled,
    area is increases 4 times.

2. Radius = 21 cm
    Diameter = 42 cm

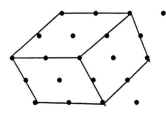

    Vol = 8 units³

Page 75
A
Page 76
1. 6
    1
    Monday
    Twice

    Tues   ☂ ☂ ☂

    Wed   ☂

    Thurs

    Fri   ☂ ☂ ☂

    Sat   ☂ ☂

    Sun   ☂

Page 77

Boys	Girls	Lessons
Charles	Elizabeth	Art
Colin	Elsie	Cookery
Derek	Jane	Computer
Edward	Jennifer	studies
Gareth	Joanne	Geography
John	Margaret	History
Paul	Rose	Maths
Raymond	Sarah	Music
Richard		Nature
		study
		PE
		Science

Pop	Nature	Sport	Horror
10	6	16	8

8
sport
nature

Page 78

	s. bacon	plain	s/v	onion
Mon	3	6	8	4
Tues	2	4	6	2
Wed	5	3	2	2
Thurs	3	5	6	3
Fri	7	7	8	3
	20	25	30	14

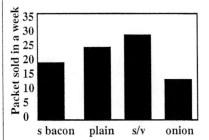

salt and vinegar
onion
89

Page 79
1. 45 min
    25 min
    8.45 am
    6.15 pm

2. 20
    29
    16
    65

Page 80
1.   C   B
        20
                11
                4

20 cars turn off at C
11 lorries pass B
15 out of 75, i.e. 20%

2. 80%
    £1 250 per tonne

Page 81
1.

3		13		21	mile
	12·5		25		km

2. vanilla
    chocolate
    raspberry and strawberry

Page 82

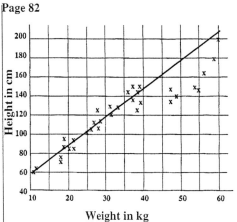

Weight in kg

1. between 35 and 40 kg
    100 and 125cm
    14
    10
    33

There is only an approximate
correlation between height and
weight. Usually weight increases
as people grow taller but people
grow at different rates and some
are thinner than others.

NATIONAL CURRICULUM

MASTER FILE

MASTER FILES

published by
Domino Books (Wales) Ltd.

AN ESTABLISHED SERIES
prepared by experienced teachers

- NOTES FOR TEACHERS AND WORKSHEETS FOR PUPILS IN ONE BOOK

- COMPREHENSIVE NATIONAL CURRICULUM COVERAGE

- THERE IS NO NEED TO BUY ADDITIONAL MATERIAL

- ALL THE MATERIAL IS PHOTOCOPIABLE

- EXCELLENT VALUE

- SAVES YOU TIME AND MONEY

- VISUALLY STIMULATING

- BOOKS SPECIFICALLY DESIGNED FOR THE KEY STAGE YOU TEACH

- FULL OF TEACHING STRATEGIES AND IDEAS

- READY-TO-USE LESSONS

- FLEXIBLE RESOURCES FOR USE BY THE WHOLE CLASS, BY GROUPS OR BY INDIVIDUAL PUPILS

- TRIED AND TESTED MATERIALS

- PHOTOCOPIABLE SHEETS TO USE AS THEY ARE OR TO REDUCE OR ENLARGE

- PHOTOCOPIABLE RECORD SHEETS FOR EACH PUPIL

- NEW TITLES PUBLISHED MONTHLY

AVAILABLE FROM
Domino Books (Wales) Ltd.,
P O Box 32, Swansea SA1 1FN.
Tel. (01792) 459378   Fax. (01792) 466337
Telephone and fax orders welcome

ORDER FORM OVERLEAF

MASTER FILES
ORDER FORM

KEY STAGE 1 (Age 5 - 7)   **KEY STAGE 2 (Age 7 - 11)**   **KEY STAGE 3 (Age 11 - 14)**

Quantity	Title	ISBN	Price	Cost
	KS1 ENGLISH	1 85772 111 X	£20.00	£
	KS1 MATHEMATICS	1 85772 107 1	£20.00	£
	KS1 MENTAL MATHEMATICS	1 85772 154 3	£20.00	£
	KS1 SCIENCE	1 85772 108 X	£20.00	£
	KS1 HISTORY	1 85772 112 8	£20.00	£
	KS2 ENGLISH	1 85772 085 7	£20.00	£
	KS2 MATHEMATICS	1 85772 086 5	£20.00	£
	KS2 SCIENCE	1 85772 087 3	£20.00	£
	KS3 ENGLISH	1 85772 127 6	£20.00	£
	KS3 MATHEMATICS	1 85772 126 8	£20.00	£
	KS3 SCIENCE	1 85772 128 4	£20.00	£
HISTORY				
	KS2 Invaders and Settlers, The Celts	1 85772 067 9	£15.95	£
	KS2 Invaders and Settlers, The Romans	1 85772 070 9	£15.95	£
	KS2 Invaders and Settlers, The Vikings	1 85772 069 5	£15.95	£
	KS2 Life in Tudor Times	1 85772 076 8	£15.95	£
	KS2/KS3 Victorian Britain	1 85772 077 6	£15.95	£
TOPICS				
	KS2/KS3 Castles	1 85772 075 X	£15.95	£
	CHRISTMAS (AGES 5 - 12)	1 85772 065 2	£20.00	£
NEW FOR EARLY YEARS				
	First Steps Basic Activities in the 3Rs	1 85772 130 6	£12.50	£
	First Steps Number and Counting	1 85772 133 0	£12.50	£
	First Steps Beginning to Read	1 85772 138 1	£12.50	£
	First Steps Beginning to Write	1 85772 139 X	£12.50	£
	First Steps Beginning Mental Maths	1 85772 142 X	£12.50	£
	First Steps Mental Maths, 5 - 6 years	1 85772 143 8	£12.50	£
	First Steps Mental Maths, 6 - 7 years	1 85772 146 2	£12.50	£
	First Steps Mental Maths, 7 - 8 years	1 85772 147 0	£12.50	£
	First Steps Mental Maths 8 - 9 years	1 85772 148 9	£12.50	£
	First Steps Developing Literacy Skills 4 - 5 years	1 85772 151 9	£12.50	£
	First Steps Developing Literacy Skills 5- 6 years	1 85772 152 7	£12.50	£
	First Steps Developing Literacy Skills 6 - 7 years	1 85772 153 5	£12.50	£
	Reading and Comprehension 5 - 7 years, Book 1	1 85772 144 6	£12.50	£
	Reading and Comprehension 5 - 7 years, Book 2	1 85772 145 4	£12.50	£
			Total	£

Name/Organisation/School

Address

Post Code   **Tel.**

Contact   **Signature**

Order Number   **Date**

Available from Blackwells, Foyles Bookshop, Waterstones, Welsh Books Council, WH Smith, and all good booksellers or direct from

DOMINO BOOKS (WALES) LTD, P O BOX 32, SWANSEA SA1 1 FN.
Tel. 01792 459378   Fax. 01792 466337

All official orders must have an official requisition form attached (schools, educational establishments, LEAs, bookshops, libraries). Cheques with private orders please.